THE COLLECTED WORKS

Recent Researches in the Music of the Renaissance is one of four quarterly series (Middle Ages and Early Renaissance; Renaissance; Baroque Era; Classical Era) which make public the early music that is being brought to light in the course of current musicological research.

Each volume is devoted to works by a single composer or in a single genre of composition, chosen because of their potential interest to scholars and performers, and prepared for publication according to the standards that govern the making of all reliable historical editions.

Subscribers to this series, as well as patrons of subscribing institutions, are invited to apply for information about the "Copyright-Sharing Policy" of A-R Editions, Inc. under which the contents of this volume may be reproduced free of charge for performance use.

Correspondence should be addressed:

A-R Editions, Inc.
315 West Gorham Street
Madison, Wisconsin 53703

RECENT RESEARCHES IN THE MUSIC OF THE RENAISSANCE • VOLUMES XXVIII and XXIX

Johann de Fossa

THE COLLECTED WORKS

Edited by Egbert M. Ennulat

A-R EDITIONS, INC. • MADISON

To Margund Ennulat

ISSN 0486-123X

ISBN 0-89579-102-1

Library of Congress Cataloging in Publication Data:

Fossa, Johannes de, d. 1603.
[Works]
The collected works.

(Recent researches in the music of the Renaissance ;
v. 28-29 ISSN 0486-123X)
Words principally in Latin.
1. Sacred vocal music. 2. Vocal music.
I. Series.
M2.R2384 vol. 28-29 [M3] 780'ffl903'ls [783'.092'4]
ISBN 0-89579-102-1 78-97

Contents

Plate I. Johann de Fossa's coat of arms, taken from his patent of nobility by imperial decree of Rudolph II in 1594. (Personenselekt 80, Fossa. Bayerisches Hauptstaatsarchiv Abt. I, Allgemeines Staatsarchiv.)

Preface

The Composer

The development of the Bayerische Hofkapelle at the ducal court in Munich was an important culminating event in the music history of the late Renaissance. Orlando di Lasso, as well known to his contemporaries as to modern scholars, was the Kapellmeister of the Bayerische Hofkapelle from 1568 until his death in 1594. Johann de Fossa, a Netherlands musician and composer of the music in the present edition, was Lasso's Unterkapellmeister there. When Lasso died in 1594, Fossa succeeded Lasso as Kapellmeister.

The name "Joannes a Fossa" first appears in extant records on a will dated 1483 of an imperial chaplain of Saint-Lambert at Liège, and a Johannes de Fossa served as a children's music teacher at the Collègiale de Dinant.[1] It has not been possible to link both references to the same person or to establish a family relation between them. Pietro de Fossis,[2] one of the first directors of music at St. Mark's Cathedral in Venice during the fifteenth century, is the first known musician with the family name de Fossa who was active outside the Netherlands.

At least three persons with the name Johann de Fossa can be authenticated besides the Johann de Fossa of the Bayerische Hofkapelle. The first of these is a Johann de Fossa who preceded Johann Stadlmayr as Kapellmeister (1603-1607) of Archduke Maximilian II in Innsbruck. Schmid[3] refers to the Innsbruck Kapellmeister Johann de Fossa (who died in 1611 as Kapellmeister of the Bishop of Passau) as the son of Johann de Fossa, Kapellmeister of the Bayerische Hofkapelle in Munich, whereas Senn[4] merely suggests this family relation as a possibility. No additional evidence in support of a family relationship is known at the present time. Two other persons with this name are known to have lived at the beginning of the seventeenth century, but there is no indication that they are related to the Kapellmeister Fossa in Munich. Although the information available is not conclusive with regard to the identity or relationships of namesakes, it is reasonable to assume that most if not all persons bearing the name Fossa came from the same Netherlands family.

Very little is known about the early life of the composer of the music in the present edition. Kapellmeister Johann de Fossa died in 1603, but no exact date or place of birth can be given. The only information about Fossa's early musical training exists in Bayerische Staatsbibliothek Music Manuscript 515 where Fossa refers to Joannes Castileti (1512-1588) as his teacher. Fossa probably studied with Castileti either in Vienna, where Castileti was imperial Kapellmeister at the court from 1563-1564, or in Liège where Castileti lived both before and after his brief tenure at the Vienna court. Fossa's studies with Castileti probably took place before 1569 when Fossa was appointed to the Bayerische Hofkapelle; it is unlikely that once Fossa was under the influence of Lasso he would have been granted an extended leave for studies with a lesser composer in the Netherlands. The *Hofzahlamtsbücher*—volumes documenting the activities of the Munich court—give no information to support the theory that Fossa studied with Castileti after 1569. Fossa did make a short journey to the Netherlands in 1585, and it is possible that he met his former teacher during this visit, and that Castileti gave Fossa his *Te Deum laudamus* on this occasion.

Additional biographical information is based on the following extant sources: (A) letter of Duke Emanuele Filiberto di Savoia to his treasurer Gaspard Specht [February 12, 1557];[5] (B) entry regarding Fossa in the *Registrarbücher* of the Hofkammer in Vienna [July, 1570];[6] (C) various entries in the *Hofzahlamtsbücher* of the Bavarian Court, Munich;[7] (D) letter of Orlando di Lasso to Prince William, Duke of Bavaria [May 14, 1575];[8] (E) letter of Duke Albert V to Prince William [October 23, 1577];[9] (F) documents on the Fossa family;[10] (G) correspondence on behalf of Fossa [December 24, 1596—October, 1604].[11]

The letter (A) of Duke Emanuele Filiberto di Savoia (dated February 12, 1557, and not January 12, 1557, as stated by Charles van den Borren in his article in *Musik in Geschichte und Gegenwart*)[12] refers to a Jean de Fosses, who was a singer at the Flemish court. It is likely that the Flemish Fossa is identical with the Unterkapellmeister in Munich, who in turn was referred to as a *Bayerischen tenoristen* in an entry (B) in the *Registrarbücher* of the Hofkammer at the Viennese court.[13]

According to the *Hofzahlamtsbücher* (C), Fossa began his service at the Bavarian court as Unterkapellmeister in 1569 with an annual salary of *fl.* 180. Salaries were figured on a quarterly basis, and since Fossa received only *fl.* 45 for his services in 1569, he must have begun his work there on or after October 1, 1569.

There is no specific information regarding Fossa's duties as Lasso's Unterkapellmeister except that in 1571 Fossa was put in charge of the *Cantorey Khnaben* (choir boys who sang the discantus in the Hofkapelle). Lasso himself had overseen the choir boys during his first year in Munich (1568); Richert von Ghenua served as "Knaben precentor" (master of the choir boys) from 1569-1570, and Fossa succeeded Ghenua in this capacity in 1571.[14]

The only reference which Lasso is known to have made to Fossa is found in a letter (D) of May 14, 1575, to Prince William. In this letter, Lasso refers to a singer brought back from Rome by Fossa. Fossa's trip to Rome is also recorded in the 1575 volume of the *Hofzahlamtsbücher.* Consequently, Fossa must have traveled to Rome at the beginning of 1575 and returned to Munich before May 14th of that year.

The last reference to Fossa before his appointment as successor to Lasso is found in a letter written by Albert V to his son William V on October 23, 1577 (E). Out of context and with no other reference, this source does not yield any real information about Fossa: "The action regarding Fossa we shall postpone until our safe return."[15] Fossa's annual salary had increased to *fl.* 300 in 1591, and *fl.* 540 for the years between 1592-1594. In 1595 his salary was *fl.* 550, and from 1596-1600 Fossa's yearly salary had increased to *fl.* 560.

Fossa was not officially referred to as Kapellmeister until 1597.[16] Although the promotion to the highest position at the Bayerische Hofkapelle did not result in a salary raise for Fossa, his elevation in 1594 to the *Reichsadelsstand* (a degree of lower nobility) by an imperial decree of Rudolf II (see Plate I) indicates the high esteem in which he was held at court.

Portions of separate correspondences on Fossa's behalf (G), dated 1596, 1597, and 1598, respectively, and preserved in the Staatsarchiv für Oberbayern in the source HR 466/446, give the most detailed account currently available of Fossa's life at court. The first of these is a letter of December 24, 1596, to Duke William V. A request is made by the anonymous writer, possibly a clerk of the ducal Hofkammer or Hofzahlamt, to remunerate Fossa for the care of the choir boys in his house during the last two quarters of the year 1596. In a second document, reference is made again to Fossa's grievance that he had not "received even one penny for an entire year [March 31, 1596—March 31, 1597] for his care of the choir boys, such as room, board and all the trouble he had with them." On the same sheet of this document an account of May 10, 1597 (in the same handwriting) reports the settlement. The Hofkammer agreed to pay Fossa *fl.* 50 for keeping the boys in his home; payment of these *fl.* 50 to Fossa is recorded in the *Hofzahlamtsbücher.*[18] Even though this payment must have been made retroactively to Fossa in 1597, the *Hofzahlamtsbücher* record it in the volume of the year 1596.

A similar situation is described in a third document dated September 7, 1598. The *Hofzahlamtsbuch* of 1598 records the settlement of a request for compensation with a payment of *fl.* 50 for the choir boys' rooms between March 31, 1597, and March 31, 1598, and an additional *fl.* 20 for rooms from April 1, 1598, to Michaelis [September 29] 1598.

The last of these documents is the formal approval of admission (dated October [?] 13, 1604) of a Hans Ludwig de Fossa as a choir boy to the Bayerische Hofkapelle, effective July 27, 1603.

These documents reflect the desperate financial situation of the Bavarian court, which led to the abdication of Duke William V in 1597. From 1594 on, the duke was forced to reduce all of his employees' salaries by half. It should be noted, however, that the difference was compensated for retroactively.

The *Hofzahlamtsbücher* record the wedding of a son of the Unterkapellmeister in 1586. Van den Borren has assigned the name Renerus to that son, but no information can be found to verify this assumption. This record of marriage, combined with an entry in a short family document (F) that gives the name, date, and hour of birth for some of Fossa's descendants born between 1588 and 1600, leads to the belief that the Hans Ludwig de Fossa referred to above was the grandson of Johann de Fossa. Document (F) establishes Hans Ludwig's birthdate as October 7, 1592; the years of birth of six others who were probably Johann de Fossa's grandchildren are also recorded in the family document as 1588, 1589, 1591, 1594, 1595, and 1600.

In summary, Fossa was connected with the Bayerische Hofkapelle from 1569-1594 as an associate and, from 1594 on, as the successor to Orlando di Lasso. Even though Fossa's tenure at the court in Munich is much better documented than his life before 1569, the information available on this composer is sketchy at best. In view of Fossa's social standing at this court, the lack of information is surprising. All of the documents cited above give only factual information and do not reveal anything about Fossa's reputation at the Bavarian court or among the musicians of the Hofkapelle. It is also impossible to find any evidence concerning Lasso's estimate of his Unterkapellmeister. Nevertheless, the extended length of their professional relationship supports the belief that Lasso valued Fossa's service. We may never know exactly what Fossa's attitude was toward his superior, and it is noteworthy that Fossa used only one of Lasso's compositions in his parodies (Fossa's Mass *Si du malheur* is based on a chanson with the same title by Lasso).

No doubt, Fossa's position in the shadow of a genius who enjoyed great fame even during his own lifetime must have influenced his relationship with Lasso. However, Fossa's work shows him to be an important composer in his own right and one who, by the idiomatic use of the continuo, developed his style beyond that of Orlando di Lasso.

Sources

The extant music of Johann de Fossa consists of six Masses, one Magnificat, three Latin antiphons, two Litanies, five sacred concerti, one Italian madrigal, and one German song. The present edition contains all the known works by Johann de Fossa as well as an anonymous antiphon, *Vidi aquam.*

Much of Fossa's music is preserved in several late sixteenth-century manuscripts. These manuscripts are presently held by the Bayerische Staatsbibliothek and recognized by the following sigla: (1) Mus. Ms. 2757 [six Masses and the anonymous antiphon *Vidi aquam*]; (2) Mus. Ms. 515 [Magnificat]; (3) Mus. Ms. 32 [three Latin antiphons]; (4) Mus. Ms. 14 [two Litanies]. With the exception of Mus. Ms. 515, which originally belonged to the monastery of Tegernsee, these manuscripts were part of the holdings of the Bayerische Hofkapelle collected from the time of Senfl (d. 1555) to that of Lasso; according to J. J. Maier, seventy-four choir books from the repertoire of the Hofkapelle, including the Fossa manuscripts, are now preserved in the Bayerische Staatsbibliothek.[19]

Fossa's five sacred concerti, as well as the Italian madrigal and the German song, exist only as portions of printed collections. These collections date from the late sixteenth and early seventeenth centuries.[20] The printed sources are listed below:

1. Viridarium musico-marianum. Concentus ecclesiasticos plus quam ducentos, in dialogo, II. III. et IV. vocum, . . . Opera et studio Joannis Denfridi . . . —Trier, L. Zetzner, 1627.

(Bibliothèque Nationale.—5 part books.—No. CXLIX: *Adiuro vos filiae;* No. CLXXXVIII: *Stabat Mater;* No. CXLVII: *Veni dilecte mi*). [RISM 1727[2]].

2. Promptuari musici concentus ecclesiasticos CCLXXXVI. selectissimos, II. III. & IV. vocum . . . D. Martini ibidem musices moderatoris.—Strasbourg, P. Ledertz, 1627.

(Bayerische Staatsbibliothek, 4° Mus. Pr. 45/1.—5 part books.—No. VVI: *Missus est;* No. CXXXVIII: *Petrus Apostolus*). [RISM 1627[1]].

3. Rosetum Marianum . . . mit fünff Stimmen componirt, und letzlich zusammen getragen. Durch Bernhardum Klingenstein . . . —Dillingen, A. Meltzer, 1604.

(Bayerische Staatsbibliothek, 4° Mus. Pr. 20/8.—5 part books.—No. I: *Maria zart*). [RISM 1604[7]].

4. Sdegnosi ardori . . . Giulio Gigli da Immola.—München, A. Berg, 1585.

(Bayerische Staatsbibliothek, 4° Mus. Pr. 44/12.—5 part books.—No. XXI: *Ardo si*). [RISM 1585[17]].

The three Latin antiphons are specifically dated in the manuscript (Palm Sunday, March 20, 1584). The composition dates of some of Fossa's other works can be estimated from the compilation dates of their sources. Compilation dates of their sources show that the six Masses and the anonymous antiphon *Vidi aquam* were composed before 1588, the Magnificat after 1563, the Italian madrigal *Ardo si* before 1585, and at least one of the two Litanies (Mus. Ms. 14, fol. 153v-157r) before 1596. Fossa's five sacred concerti and his setting of the German song *Maria zart* cannot be specifically dated because they have been preserved only in posthumous prints of the early seventeenth century.

The antiphon *Vidi aquam* has been included in this edition because it is the only anonymous composition in the most important single source of Fossa's music, Mus. Ms. 2757. In this manuscript Fossa's Mass VI and the anonymous composition are written in the hand of the same scribe. In addition to general stylistic similarities, a specific relationship exists between Fossa's three Latin antiphons of Mus. Ms. 32 and *Vidi aquam* in the use of the descending minor sixth, which is found twice in the Mus. Ms. 32 antiphons (antiphon I, m. 8, superius; antiphon III, m. 24, altus) and once in *Vidi aquam* (m. 50, altus). In all instances the two notes of the descending minor sixth are set apart by a comma in the text. Both the antiphons of Mus. Ms. 32 and *Vidi aquam* are based on plainchant material that is treated with great liberty; portions of the *cantus firmus* are utilized throughout all voices. Some details of notation (a *podatus*-like ligature and a half-coloration in the superius of m. 55 and altus m. 57, respectively), which do not occur elsewhere in Fossa's compositions, could be advanced as arguments against Fossa's authorship of *Vidi aquam.*

The Edition

Note values are reduced by half throughout this edition in order to reflect the original tempo as intended by the composer, and to provide a score suitable for performance. The triple meter sections throughout *Stabat Mater dolorosa, Petrus Apostolus,* and *Missus est Angelus Gabriel* appear with a 3/2 time signature in the source even though there are three semibreves to a measure.

For scholarly reference and clarity, incipits are used in the present edition. A full incipit, including the original clef, key, and time signatures as well as the first note in its durational value, appears at the beginning of each self-contained movement. Partial incipits, including everything mentioned above except the first note, are given when the number of voices changes within a work; partial incipits also appear at the beginnings of new sections of text (e.g., Gloria, Credo, etc. in the Masses) within self-contained works. Ligatures and colorations are marked with horizontal brackets and broken brackets, respectively. Repeated original accidentals are omitted where they would be redundant within the same measure and voice. *Musica ficta* modifications are indicated by accidentals in square brackets, which precede the affected notes and hold through the entire measure in the same voice. Accidentals in square brackets are also added to originally uninflected notes which are directly preceded in the same measure and voice by the same note with an original accidental. Cautionary accidentals—enclosed in parentheses—are given when a note reflecting the key signature is immediately preceded in the previous measure in the same voice by an inflected note on the same line or space, or when a note is preceded in the same measure, but in a different voice, by an inflected note of the same pitch.

In the figured-bass realization of the five sacred concerti, editorial accidentals in square brackets are added to notes of the bass line when this inflection is implied by the vocal parts.

Editorial text repetitions are indicated by square brackets, and the occurrence of two syllables on one note is marked by a slur. For the sake of unity the original text versions of the upper voice in the German song and Italian madrigal have been adopted for all voice parts. In addition, punctuation (and capitalizations after periods) has been added in *Maria zart* in order to clarify the text.[21] Latin texts have been modernized according to the *Liber Usualis.* In the Litanies, Fossa omitted the last four petitions before the *Agnus Dei,* as well as the petition *Mater boni consilii.*

Acknowledgments

I express my thanks to Dr. Edward G. Evans, Jr., for his generous help and encouragement and to the Bayerische Staatsbibiothek for furnishing the microfilms for this edition.

Egbert M. Ennulat
University of Georgia
Athens, Georgia

September 1977

Notes

[1]Antoine Auda, *La Musique et les Musiciens de l'Ancien Pays de Liège* (Bruxelles: Librairie Saint-Georges, 1930), p. 121.

[2]Fabio Fano and Friedrich Blume, "Venedig," *Die Musik in Geschichte und Gegenwart,* XIII (1966): 1373.

[3]Ernst Fritz Schmid, *Musik an den schwäbischen Zollernhöfen der Renaissance* (Kassel: Bärenreiter, 1962), p. 481.

[4]Walter Senn, *Musik und Theater am Hof zu Innsbruck* (Innsbruck: Östereichische Verlagsanstalt, 1954), p. 188.

[5]S. Cordero di Pamparato, "Emanuele Filiberto di Savoia protettore dei musici," *Rivista Musicale Italiana,* XXXIV (1927): 560.

[6]Albert Smijers, *Die Kaiserliche Hofmusik-Kapelle von 1543 bis 1619* (Wien: Universal-Edition, 1922), p. 85.

[7]Adolf Sandberger, *Beiträge zur Geschichte der Bayerischen Hofkapelle unter Orlando di Lasso,* vols. I, III (Leipzig: Breitkopf & Härtel, 1894-1895), III: 241-244.

[8]Sandberger, *Beiträge,* III: 271.

[9]Sandberger, *Beiträge,* III: 313.

[10]*Personenselekt 80, Fossa.* Preserved at the *Bayerisches Hauptstaatsarchiv Abt. I, Allgemeines Staatsarchiv.* This source contains the following documents: (1) general information on the Fossa family 1588-1600 (three small pages); (2) general information on descendants of the Fossa family 1651-1659 (six small pages); (3) miscellaneous documents on descendants of the Fossa family ca. 1632—ca. 1750; (4) Reichsadelsbrief of 1594 (imperial patent of nobility).

[11]HR 466/446, preserved in the *Staatsarchiv für Oberbayern.* This compound source contains the following documents: (G1) letter to the Duke of Bavaria, dated December 24, 1596; (G2) communication on behalf of Fossa, dated March 6, 1597 and May 10, 1597 respectively; (G3) petition to the Hofkammer in Fossa's behalf, dated September 7, 1598; (G4) communication about the admission of Hans Ludwig de Fossa as a choir boy to the Bayerische Hofkapelle, dated October [?] 13, 1604.

[12]Charles van den Borren, "Fossa," *Die Musik in Geschichte und Gegenwart,* IV (1955): 588.

[13]Albert Smijers, *Die Kaiserliche Hofmusik-Kapelle,* p. 85: "E. Nr. 287, f. 241: Juli 1570: Joanni de Fossa bayerischen tenoristen haben Jr Mt. etc umb das er deren ain mess verehrt, 30 fl. aus gnaden zu geben verordnet." (His Majesty graciously ordered that Joanni de Fossa, Bavarian tenor, be paid 30 fl. for a Mass which he had dedicated to him).

[14]Sandberger, *Beiträge,* III: 56.

[15]Sandberger, *Beiträge,* III: 313: "Die Handlung den Fossa betreffend stellen wir also bis zu unnserer, wills Gott, glückhlichen anheimbskonft in rhue. . . ."

[16]Sandberger, *Beiträge,* III: 194-233.

[17]*Personenselekt 80, Fossa.*

[18]Sandberger, *Beiträge,* III: 227.

[19]Julius Joseph Maier, *Die Musikalischen Handschriften der K. Hof- und Staatsbibliothek in München* (München: Palm'sche Hofbuchhandlung, 1879), I: 71.

[20]For detailed information on all known sources of Fossa's music and the model compositions for his parody Masses and Magnificat, see Egbert Ennulat, "Johann de Fossa and his Work" (Ph.D. diss., Case Western Reserve University, 1971), I: 36-65, obtainable from University Microfilms, Ann Arbor, No. 72-6287.

[21]For another text version and an English translation see Gustave Reese, *Music in the Renaissance* (New York: W. W. Norton, 1954), p. 193.

Plate II. Johann de Fossa: *Magnificat Vivre ne puis sur terre,* two opening pages; Mus. Ms. 515, fol. 1v, 2r. (Courtesy Bayerische Staatsbibliothek.)

THE COLLECTED WORKS

Missa Era di mayo

Kyrie

20
-son, Ky- ri- e e- - lei- son.
-son, Ky- ri- e e- leï- - son, Ky- ri- e e- lei- son.
e- lei- son, e- - lei- son, Ky- rie e- lei- son.
-son, Ky- ri- e e- - lei- son.
Gloria
5
Et in ter- ra pax ho- mi- ni- bus bo- - nae vo- lun- ta- tis.
Et in ter- ra pax ho- mi- ni- bus bo- nae vo- lun- ta- tis. Lau-da-mus
Et in ter- ra pax ho- mi- ni-bus bo- nae vo-lun - ta- tis. Lau- da- mus
Et in ter- ra pax ho- mi- ni- bus bo- nae vo- lun- ta- tis. Lau- da- mus
Be- ne- di- ci- mus te. Ad - o- ra- mus te. Glo- ri- fi- ca- - mus te. Gra-
te. Be- ne- di- ci- mus te. Ad - o- ra- mus te. Glo- ri- fi- ca- mus te. Gra- ti- as,
te. Be- ne- di- ci- mus te. Ad - o- ra- mus te. Glo- ri- fi- ca- mus te.
te. Be- ne- di- ci- mus te. Glo- ri- fi- ca- mus te.
10
- ti- as, gra- ti- as a- gi- mus ti- bi pro- pter ma- gnam glo- - ri- am tu-
gra- ti- as a- gi- mus ti- bi pro- pter ma- gnam glo- ri- am tu-
Gra- ti- as a- gi- mus ti- bi pro- pter ma- gnam glo- ri- am tu-
Gra- ti- as a- gi- mus ti- bi pro- pter ma- gnam glo- ri- am tu- am.

15
-am. De- us Pa- ter o-mni- po-tens.
-am. De- us Pa- ter o- mni- po- tens. Do-
-am. Do- mi- ne De-us, Rex cae-le- stis, De- us Pa- ter o-mni- potens. Do-
Do- mi- ne De-us, Rex cae-le- stis, Do-
20
u- ni- ge- ni- te Je- su Chri- ste. Do-mi- ne De-
-mi- ne Fi- li u- ni- ge- ni- te Je- su Chri- ste. Do- mi- ne De-
-mi- ne Fi- li u- ni- ge- ni- te Je- su Chri- ste.
-mi- ne Fi- li- u- ni- ge- ni- te Je- su Chri- ste. Do- mi- ne De-
25
-us, A- gnus De- i, Fi- li- us Pa- tris. Qui tol- lis pec- ca- ta
-us, A- gnus De- i, Fi- li- us Pa- tris. Qui tol- lis pec- ca-
Agnus De- i, Fi- li- us Pa- tris. Qui tol- lis pec- ca- ta
-us, A- gnus De- i, Fi- li- us Pa- tris. Qui tol- lis pec- ca-
30
mun- di, mi- se- re- re no- bis. Qui tol- lis pec- ca- ta mun- di, sus-
-ta mun- di, mi- se- re- re no- bis. Qui tol- lis pec- ca- - ta mun-di, sus-
mun- di, mi- se- re- re no- bis. Qui tol- lis pec- ca- ta mun- di, sus-
-ta mun- di, mi- se- re- re no- bis. Qui tol- lis pec- ca- ta mun- di, sus-

- ci- pe de- pre-ca- ti - o-nem no- stram.Qui se- des ad dex- te- ram Pa- tris, mi- se-
- ci- pe de- pre-ca- ti - o-nem no- stram.Qui se- des ad dex- te- ram Pa- tris, mi- se-
- ci- pe de- pre-ca- ti - o- nem no- stram. Qui se- des ad dex- te- ram Pa- tris, mi- se-
- ci- pe de- pre-ca- ti - o- nem no- stram. Qui se- des mi- se-
35
-re- re no- bis. Quo- ni- am tu so- lus san- ctus. Tu so- lus Do- - mi- nus, Je-
-re- re no- bis. Quo- ni- am tu so- lus san- ctus. Tu so- lus Do- mi- nus, Je-
-re- re no- bis. Quo- ni- am tu so- lus san- ctus. Tu so- lus Al- tis- si-
-re- re no- bis. Quo- ni- am tu so- lus san- ctus. Tu so- lus Al- tis- si-
40
- su Chri- ste. Cum San- cto Spi- ri- tu, in glo- ri- a De- i Pa- - tris.A- men.
- su Chri- ste. Cum San- cto Spi- ri- tu, in glo- ri- a De- i Pa- tris. A- men.
-mus, Je- su Chri- ste. Cum San-cto Spi- ri- tu, in glo- ri- a De- i Pa- tris. A- men.
-mus, Je- su Chri- ste. Cum San- cto Spi- ri- tu, in glo- ri- a De- i Pa- tris. A- men.

Credo

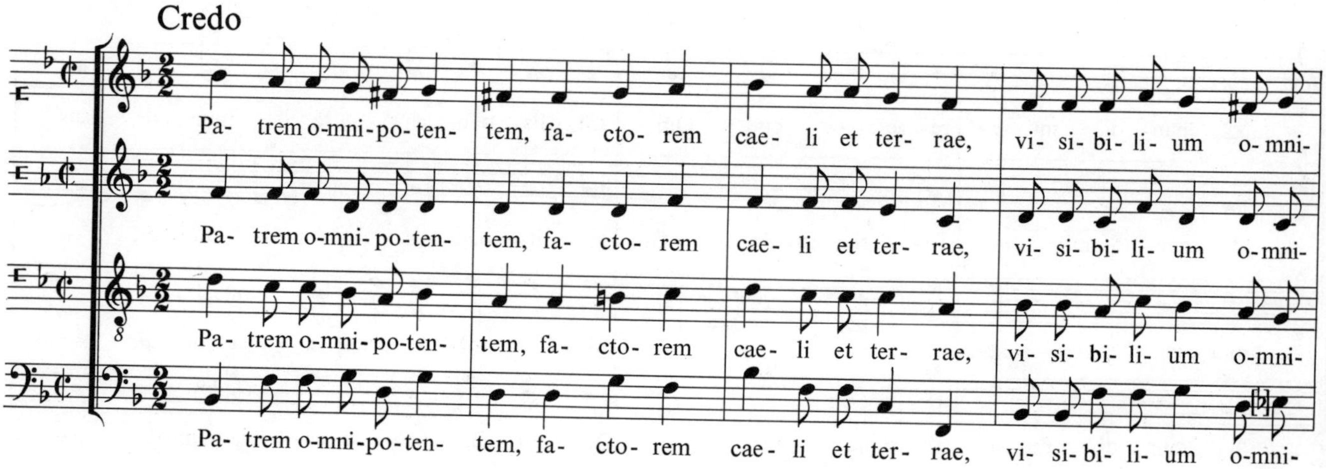
Pa- trem o-mni- po- ten- tem, fa- cto- rem cae- li et ter- rae, vi- si- bi- li- um o- mni-
Pa- trem o-mni- po- ten- tem, fa- cto- rem cae- li et ter- rae, vi- si- bi- li- um o- mni-
Pa- trem o-mni- po- ten- tem, fa- cto- rem cae- li et ter- rae, vi- si- bi- li- um o- mni-
Pa- trem o-mni-po- ten- tem, fa- cto- rem cae- li et ter- rae, vi- si- bi- li- um o- mni-

5
-um et in-vi-si-bi-li-um. Et in u-num Do-mi-num Je-sum Chri-stum,
-um et in-vi-si-bi-li-um. Et in u-num Do-mi-num Je-sum Chri-stum,
-um et in-vi-si-bi-li-um. Et in u-num Do-mi-num Je-sum Chri-stum,
-um et in-vi-si-bi-li-um. Je-sum Chri-stum,
10
Fi-li-um De-i u-ni-ge-ni tum. Et ex Pa-tre na-tum an-te o-mni-a sae-cu-
Fi-li-um De-i u-ni-ge-ni-tum. Et ex Pa-tre na-tum an-te o-mni-a sae-cu-
Fi-li-um De-i u-ni-ge-ni-tum. Et ex Pa-tre na-tum an-te o-mni-a sae-cu-
Fi-li-um De-i u-ni-ge-ni-tum. Et ex Pa-tre na-tum
15
-la. De-um de De-o, lu-men de lu-mi-ne,
-la. De-um de De-o, lu-men de lu-mi-ne, De-um ve-rum de De-o ve-ro.
-la. De-um de De-o, lu-men de lu-mi-ne, De-um ve-rum de De-o ve-ro.
De-um de De-o, lu-men de lu-mi-ne, De-um ve-rum de De-o ve-ro.
20
Ge-ni-tum, non fa-ctum, con-sub-stan-ti-a-lem Pa-tri: per quem o-mni-
Ge-ni-tum, non fa-ctum, con-sub-stan-ti-a-lem Pa-tri: per quem o-mni-
Ge-ni-tum, non fa-ctum, con-sub-stan-ti-a-lem Pa-tri: per quem o-mni-
con-sub-stan-ti-a-lem Pa-tri: per quem o-mni-

-a fa- cta sunt. et pro-pter no- stram sa-lu- tem de-
-a fa- cta sunt. Qui pro-pter nos ho-mi-nes, et pro-pter no-stram sa- lu- tem
-a fa- cta sunt. Qui pro-pter nos ho-mi-nes, et pro-pter no- stram sa-lu- tem de-
-a fa- cta sunt. Qui pro- pter nos ho-mi-nes,
25
30
- scen-dit de cae- lis. Et in- car- na- tus est de Spi- ri-
de- scen-dit de cae- lis. Et in- car- na- tus est de Spi- ri-
- scen-dit de cae- lis. Et in- car- na- tus est de Spi- ri- tu
de- scen- dit de cae- lis. Et in- car- na- tus est de Spi- ri-
35
-tu San- cto ex Ma- ri- a Vir- - gi- ne: Et ho-
-tu San- cto ex Ma- ri- a Vir- gi- ne: Et ho-
San- cto ex Ma- ri- a Vir- - gi ne: Et
-tu San- cto ex Ma- ri- a Vir- - gi- ne: Et ho-
-mo fa- ctus est.
- mo fa- ctus est.
ho- mo fa- ctus est. Cru- ci- fi- xus e- ti- am pro no- bis: sub
- mo fa- ctus est. Cru- ci- fi- xus e- ti- am pro no- bis: sub Pon-ti-

40
pas- sus, et se- pul- tus est. Et re-sur-re- xit ter-ti- a di-
pas- sus, et se- pul- tus est. Et re-sur-re- xit ter- ti- a di-
Pon-ti- o Pi- la- to pas- sus, et se- pul- tus est. ter- ti- a di-
-o Pi- la- to pas- sus, et se- pul- tus est.
45
-e, se- cun- dum Scri- ptu- ras. Et a- scen- dit in cae- lum: se-
-e, se- cun- dum Scri- ptu- ras. Et a- scen- dit in cae- lum: se-
-e, se- cun- dum Scri- ptu- ras. Et a- scen- dit in cae- lum: se-
Et a- scen- dit in cae- lum:
50
-det ad dex- te- ram Pa- tris. ven- tu- rus est cum glo- ri- a, ju-
-det ad dex- te- ram Pa- tris. Et i- te- rum ven- tu- rus est cum glo- ri- a,
-det ad dex- te- ram Pa- tris. Et i- te- rum ven- tu- rus est cum glo- ri- a,
ven- tu- rus est cum glo- ri- a,
- di- ca- re vi- vos et mor- tu- os: cu- jus re- gni non e- rit fi-
ju- di- ca- re vi- vos et mor- tu- os: cu- jus re- gni non e- rit fi-
ju- di- ca- re vi- vos et mor- tu- os: cu- jus re- gni non e- rit fi-
ju- di- ca- re vi- vos et mor- tu- os: cu- jus re- gni non e- rit fi-

55
-nis. Et in Spi- ri- tum San- ctum, Do- mi- num, et vi- vi- fi- can- tem:
-nis. Et in Spi- ri- tum San- ctum, Do- mi- num, et vi- vi- fi- can- tem:
-nis. Et in Spi- ri- tum San- ctum, Do- mi- num, et vi- vi- fi- can- tem:
-nis. Et in Spi- ri- tum San- ctum, Do- mi- num,
60
qui ex Pa- tre, Fi- li- o- que pro- ce- dit. Qui cum Pa- tre et Fi- li- o si- mul
qui ex Pa- tre, Fi- li- o- que pro- ce- dit. Qui cum Pa- tre et Fi- li- o si- mul
qui ex Pa- tre, Fi- li- o- que pro- ce- dit. Qui cum Pa- tre et Fi- li- o si- mul
qui ex Pa- tre, Fi- li- o- que pro- ce- dit. si- mul
65
ad- o- ra- tur, et con- glo- ri- fi- ca- tur: qui lo- cu- tus est per Pro- phe-
ad- o- ra- tur, et con- glo- ri- fi- ca- tur: qui lo- cu- tus est per Pro- phe-
ad- o- ra- tur, et con- glo- ri- fi- ca- tur: qui lo- cu- tus est per Pro- phe-
ad- o- ra- tur, et con- glo- ri- fi- ca- tur: qui lo- cu- tus est per Pro- phe-
-tas. Et u- nam san- ctam ca- tho- li- cam et a- po- sto- li- cam Ec- cle- si- am. Con-
-tas. Et u- nam san- ctam ca- tho- li- cam et a- po- sto- li- cam Ec- cle- si- am.
- tas. et a- po- sto- li- cam Ec- cle- si- am. Con-
-tas. et a- po- sto- li- cam Ec- cle- si- am. Con-

70
-fi- te- or u- num ba- pti- sma in re-mis-si- o- nem pec- ca- to-
u- num ba- pti- sma in re-mis-si- o- nem pec- ca- to-
-fi- te- or u- num ba- pti- sma in re-mis-si- o- nem pec- ca-
-fi- te- or u- num ba- pti- sma in re-mis-si- o- nem pec- ca- to-
75
- rum. Et ex- spe- cto re- - sur- re- cti- o- nem mor- tu- o-
-rum. Et ex- spe- cto re- - sur- re- cti- o- nem mor- tu- o-
-to- rum. Et ex- spe- cto re- - sur- re- cti- o- nem mor- tu- o-
-rum. Et ex- spe- cto mor- tu- o-
80
-rum. Et vi- tam ven- tu- ri sae- cu- li. A- men.
-rum. Et vi- tam ven- tu- ri sae- cu- li. A- men.
-rum. Et vi- tam ven- tu- ri sae- cu- li. A- men.
-rum. Et vi- tam ven- tu- ri sae- cu- li. A- men.

Sanctus

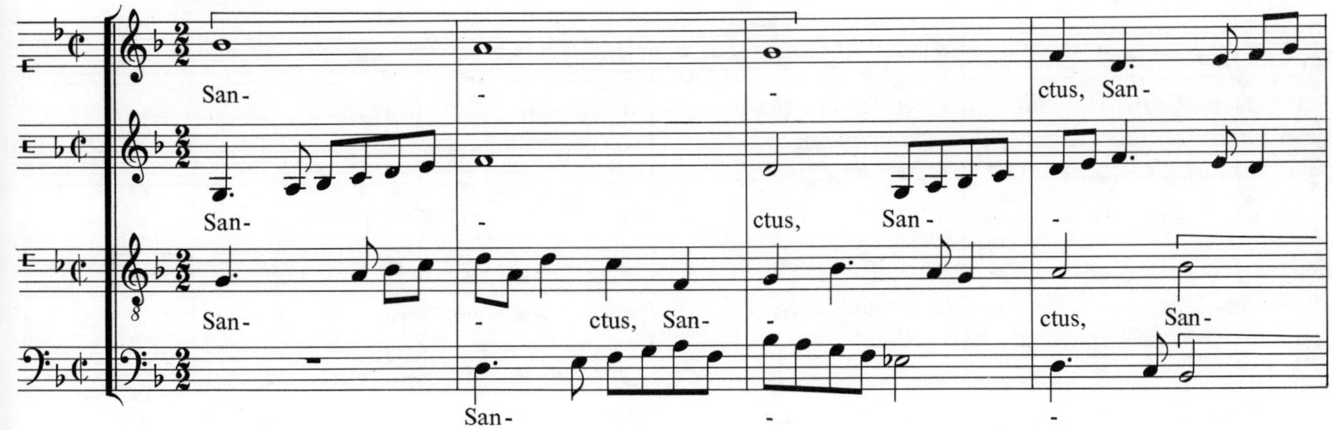
San- - - ctus, San-
San- - ctus, San- -
San- - ctus, San- - ctus, San-
San- - -

- - ctus, San- - ctus, San- -
- ctus, San- - ctus, San-
- - ctus, San- -
-ctus, San- - - ctus, San- ctus,
-ctus Do- - mi- nus De- us Sa-
- - ctus Do- mi- nus De- us Sa- ba- oth,
- - ctus Do- mi- nus De- us Sa- ba- oth, Do- mi-
San- - ctus Do- mi- nus
- ba- oth. Ple- ni sunt cae- li, et ter- -
Sa- ba- oth. Ple- ni sunt cae- li, et ter- -
-nus De- us Sa- ba- oth. Ple- ni sunt cae- li, ple- ni sunt cae- li et
De- us Sa- ba- oth. Ple- ni sunt cae- li et ter- ra
-ra glo- ri- a tu- a, et ter-ra glo- ri- a tu- a.
-ra glo- ri- a tu- - a, glo- - ri- a tu- a.
ter- ra glo- ri- a tu- a, glo- ri- a tu- a.
glo- ri- a tu- a, glo- ri- a tu- a.

25
Be- - ne- di- ctus qui
Be- - ne- - di- ctus,
Be- - ne- di- ctus, Be-
ve- nit in no- mi- ne
Be- ne- di- ctus qui ve-
- - ne- di- ctus qui ve- nit in
30
Do- - mi- ni, in no- mi- ne,
-nit in no- mi- ne, in no- mi- ne
no- mi- ne Do- - mi- ni,
35
in no- mi- ne Do- - mi- ni.
Do- mi- ni, in no- mi- ne Do- - mi- ni.
in no- mi- ne Do- mi- ni.

40
Ho- san- na in ex- - cel- sis, Ho- san- na in
Ho- san- na in ex- - cel- sis, Ho- san- na in ex- cel-
Ho- san- na in ex- - cel- sis, Ho- san- na in ex-
Ho- san- na in ex- cel- sis, Ho- san-
45
ex- cel- sis, in ex- cel- sis, Ho- san- na in
-sis, Ho- san- na in ex- cel- sis, Ho- san-
- - cel- sis, Ho- san- na in ex- cel- sis,
-na in ex- cel- sis, Ho- san- na in ex-
50
ex- cel- sis.
-na in ex- cel- sis, Ho- san- na in ex- cel- sis.
Ho- san- na in ex- cel- - sis.
- cel- sis, Ho- san- na in ex- cel- sis.

Agnus Dei

A- gnus De- i, qui tol- lis pec- ca- - ta mun-
-di: mi- se- re- re no- bis, mi- se-
-re re no- - bis.
A- gnus De- i, qui tol- lis pec- ca- - ta mun-
-di: mi- - se- re- re no- bis, mi- se- re- re no-
-bis, mi- - se- re- - re no- bis.
A- gnus De- i, qui tol- lis pec- ca- - ta mun-
-di: mi- se- re- - re no- -
- bis, mi- se- re- re no- bis.
A- gnus De- i, qui tol- lis pec- ca- - ta mun-
-di: mi- - se- re- - re no-
-bis, mi- se- re- re no- bis.
5
10

Missa Ich segge â dieu

20
Ky- ri- e e- - lei- son.
- ri- e e- lei- son, Ky- ri- e e- lei- son.
-son, Ky- ri- e e- lei- son, e- lei- son.
-ri- e e- lei- son, Ky- ri- e e- lei- son.

Gloria

5
Et in ter- ra pax ho-mi- ni- bus bo- nae vo- lun- ta- tis.
Et in ter- ra pax ho- mi- ni- bus bo- nae vo- lun- ta- tis. Lau- da- mus
Et in ter- ra pax ho- mi- ni- bus bo- nae vo- lun- ta- tis. Lau-da- mus
Et in ter- ra pax ho- mi- ni- bus bo- nae vo- lun- ta- tis. Be-
Be- ne- di- ci- mus te. Ad- o- ra- mus te. Glo- ri- fi- ca-mus te. Gra- ti- as
te. Be- ne- di- ci- mus te. Ad- o- ra- mus te. Glo- ri- fi- ca-mus te. Gra-ti-
te. Be- ne- di- ci- mus te. Ad- o- ra- mus te. Glo- ri- fi- ca-mus te. Gra-ti-
-ne- di- ci-mus te. Ad- o- ra- mus te. Gra-ti- as
10
a- gi- mus ti- bi pro-pter ma- gnam glo- ri- am tu- am. Do- mi- ne De- - us, Rex
-as a- gi-mus ti- bi pro-pter ma-gnam glo- ri- am tu- am. Do- mi- ne De-
-as a- gi-mus ti- bi pro-pter ma-gnam glo- ri- am tu- am. Do- mi- ne De- us, Rex
a- gi-mus ti- bi pro-pter ma- gnam glo- ri- am tu- am. Do- mi- ne De- - us, Rex cae-

15
cae- le- stis, De- us Pa- ter o- mni- po- tens. Do- mi-ne Fi- li- u- ni-ge-ni-te
us Rex cae-le- stis, De- us Pa- ter Do- - mi-ne Fi- li u- - ni-ge-ni-te
cae- le- stis, De- us Pa- ter o- mni- po- tens. Do-mi-ne Fi- li u- ni-ge-ni- te
- le- stis, De-us Pa- ter o- mni po- tens.
20
25
Je- su Chri- ste. Do- mi-ne De- us, A- - gnus De- i, Fi- li- us Pa- tris.
Je- su Chri- ste. Do- mi-ne De- us, A- gnus De- i, Fi-li-us Pa- tris.
Je- su Chri- ste. Do- mi- ne De- us, A-gnus De- i, Fi- li- us Pa- tris.
Je- su Chri- ste. Do- mi- ne De- us, A- gnus De- i, Fi- li- us Pa- tris.
30
Qui tol- lis pec- ca- ta mun- di, mi- se- re-re no- bis. Qui tol- lis pec- ca-
Qui tol- lis pec- ca- ta mun- di, mi- se - re-re no-bis. Qui tol- lis pec- ca-
Qui tol- lis pec-ca- ta mun- di, mi- se- re-re no- bis, mi- se- re- re no-bis. Qui
Qui tol- lis pec- ca- ta mun- di, Qui tol- lis pec- ca-
35
-ta mun- di, sus- ci- pe de- pre-
-ta mun- di, sus- ci- pe de- pre-ca-
tol- lis pec- ca- ta mun- di, sus- - ci-pe de- pre-ca-
-ta mun- di, sus- ci- pe de- pre-ca-

-ca- ti- o- nem no- stram. Qui se- des ad dex- te- ram Pa- tris,
-ti- o- nem no- stram. Qui se- des ad dex- te- ram Pa- tris,
-ti- o- nem no- - stram. Qui se- des ad dex- te- ram Pa- tris,
-ti- o- nem no- stram. Qui se- des
40
mi- se- re- re no- bis. Quo- ni- am tu so- lus san- ctus. Tu so- lus
mi- se- re- re no- bis. Quo- ni- am tu so- lus san- ctus. Tu so- lus
mi- se- re- re no- bis. Quo- ni am tu so- lus san- ctus. Tu so- lus
mi- se- re- re no- bis. Quo- ni- am tu so- lus san- ctus. Tu so- lus
45
Do- mi- nus. Tu so- lus Al- tis- si- mus, Je- su Chri- - ste.
Do- mi- nus. Tu so- lus Al- tis- si- mus, Je- su Chri- ste.
Do- mi- nus. Tu so- lus Al- tis- si- mus, Je- su Chri- - ste.
Do- mi- nus. Tu so- lus Al- tis- si- mus, Je- su Chri- - ste.
50
Cum San- cto Spi- ri- tu, in glo- ri- a De- i Pa- tris. A- men.
Cum San- cto Spi- ri- tu, in glo- ri- a De- i Pa- tris. A- - men.
Cum San- cto Spi- ri- tu, in glo- ri- a De- i Pa- tris. A- men.
Cum San- cto Spi- ri- tu, in glo- ri- a De- i Pa- tris. A- men.

Credo

Pa- trem o-mni-po- ten- tem, fa-cto- rem cae- li et ter- rae, vi- si-
Pa- trem o- mni-po-ten- tem, fa- cto- rem cae- li et ter- rae, vi- si-
Pa- trem o- mni-po-ten- tem, fa- cto- rem cae- li et ter- - rae, vi- si-
Pa- trem o- mni-po-ten- tem, fa- cto- rem cae- li et ter- rae, vi- si-
5
-bi- li- um o- mni- um et in- vi- si- bi- li- um. Je- sum
-bi- li- um o- mni-um et in- vi- si- bi- li- um. Je- sum Chri-
-bi- li- um o- mni-um et in- vi- si- bi- li- um. Et in u- num Do-mi- num Je- sum
-bi- li- um o- mni- um Et in u- num Do-mi- num Je- sum
10
Chri- stum, Fi- li- um De- i u- ni- ge- ni- tum. Et ex Pa- tre na- tum an- te
- stum, Fi- li- um De- i u- ni- ge-ni- tum. Et ex Pa- tre na- tum an- te
Chri- stum, Et ex Pa- tre na- tum an- te
Chri- stum, Et ex Pa- tre na- tum an- te
15
o- mni-a sae- cu- la. lu- men de lu-mi-ne, De- um ve- rum de De-o ve- ro. Ge-
o- mni-a sae- cu- la. lu- men de lu-mi- ne, De-um ve- rum de De-o ve- ro. Ge-
o- mni- a sae- cu- la. De-um de De- o, De- um ve- rum de De-o ve- ro. Ge-
o- mni-a sae- cu- la. De-um de De- o, De- um ve- rum de De-o ve- ro. Ge-

20
- ni-tum, non fa- ctum, con-sub-stan-ti- a- lem Pa- tri: per quem o- mni- a fa- cta
- ni-tum, non fa- ctum, con-sub-stan-ti- a- lem Pa- tri: per quem o- mni- a fa- cta
- ni-tum, non fa- ctum, con-sub-stan-ti- a- lem Pa- tri: per quem o- mni- a fa- cta sunt.
- ni tum, non fa- ctum, per quem o- mni- a fa- cta
25
sunt. et pro-pter no- stram sa- lu- tem de- scen- dit
sunt. et pro-pter no- stram sa- lu- - tem de-
Qui pro- pter nos ho-mi- nes, et pro-pter no- stram sa- lu- tem de- scen- dit
sunt. Qui pro-pter nos ho- mi- nes, et pro-pter no- stram sa- lu- tem de- scen- dit
30
de cae- lis. Et in- car- na- tus est de Spi- ri- tu San- cto ex
-scen- dit de cae- lis. Et in- car- na- tus est de Spi- ri- tu San- cto ex
de cae- lis. Et in- car- na- tus est de Spi- ri- tu San- - cto ex
de cae- lis. Et in- car- na- tus est de Spi- ri- tu San- cto ex
35
Ma- ri- a Vir- gi- ne: Et ho- mo fa- - ctus
Ma- ri- a Vir- gi- ne: Et ho- mo fa- ctus est.
Ma- ri- a Vir- gi- ne: Et ho- mo fa- ctus est, Et ho- mo fa- ctus
Ma- ri- a Vir- gi- ne: Et ho- mo fa- ctus est.

40
est. Cru- ci- fi- xus e- ti- am pro no- bis: sub Pon-ti- o Pi- la- to pas-
Cru- ci- fi- xus e- ti- am pro no- bis: sub Pon-ti- o Pi- la- to pas-
est. Cru- ci- fi- xus e- ti- am pro no- bis: sub Pon-ti- o Pi- la- to pas-
Cru- ci- fi- xus e- ti- am pro no- bis: sub Pon-ti- o Pi- la- to pas-
45
- sus, et se- pul- tus est. Et re-sur-re- xit ter- ti- a di- e, se-cun-dum Scri-
-sus, et se- pul- tus est. Et re-sur-re- xit ter-ti- a di- e, se-cun-dum Scri- ptu-
- sus, et se- - pul- tus est. Et re-sur-re- xit ter-ti- a di- e, se-cun-dum Scri-
- sus, et se- pul- tus est. Et re-sur-re- xit
50
-ptu- ras. Et a- scen-dit in cae- lum: se- det ad dex-te- ram Pa- tris. Et i- te-
-ras. Et a- scen- dit in cae- lum: se- det, se-det ad dex-te- ram Pa- tris. Et i- te-
-ptu- ras. Et a-scen- dit in cae- lum: se- det ad dex-te- ram Pa- tris. Et i- te-
Et i- te-
55
-rum ven-tu- rus est cum glo- ri- a, ju- di- ca- re vi- vos et mor- tu-
-rum ven-tu- rus est cum glo- ri- a, ju- di- ca- re vi- vos et mor- tu-
-rum ven-tu- rus est cum glo- ri- a, ju- di- ca- re vi- vos et mor- tu-
-rum ven-tu- rus est, ju- di- ca- re vi- vos et mor- tu-

-os: cu- -jus re- gni non e- rit fi- nis. San-ctum,Do-mi-num,
-os: cu- jus re- gni non e- rit fi- nis. San-ctum,Do-mi-num,
-os: cu- -jus re- gni non e- rit fi- nis. Et in Spi- ri- tum San- ctum,Do-mi-num,
-os: cu- -jus re- gni non e- rit fi- nis. Et in Spi- ri- tum
60
et vi- vi- fi- can- tem: Fi- li- o- que pro- ce- dit. Qui cum
et vi- vi- fi- can- tem: qui ex Pa- tre, Fi- li- o- que pro- ce- dit. Qui cum Pa-
et vi- vi- fi- can- tem: qui ex Pa- tre, Fi- li- o- que pro-ce- dit. Qui cum Pa-
et vi- vi- fi- can- tem: qui ex Pa- tre, Fi- li- o- que pro-ce- dit. Qui
65
Pa- tre et Fi- li- o si- mul ad- o- ra- tur, et con-glo- ri- fi- ca- tur:
-tre et Fi- li- o si- mul ad- o- ra- tur, et con-glo- ri- fi- ca- tur:
-tre et Fi- li- o si- mul ad- o- ra- tur, et con-glo- ri- fi- ca- tur:
cum Pa- tre et Fi- li- o si- mul ad- o- ra- tur, et con-glo- ri- fi- ca- tur:
70
qui lo- cu- tus est per Pro- phe- tas. Et u- nam san-ctam ca- tho- li- cam et a- po- sto- li-cam Ec-
qui lo- cu- tus est per Pro-phe- tas. Et u- nam san-ctam ca- tho- li- cam et a- po- sto- li- cam Ec-
qui lo- cu- tus est per Pro-phe- tas. Et u- nam san-ctam ca- tho- li- cam et a- po- sto- li- cam Ec-
Et u- nam san-ctam ca- tho- li- cam et a- po- sto- li-cam Ec-

-cle- si- am. Con- fi- te- or u- num ba- pti- sma, u- num ba- pti- sma in re- mis- si- o-
-cle- si- am. Con- fi- te- or u- num ba- pti- sma in re- mis- si- o-
-cle- si- am. Con- fi- te- or u- num ba- pti- sma in re- mis- si- o- nem
-cle- si- am. u- num ba- pti- sma in re- mis- si- o-
-nem pec- ca- to- rum. Et ex- spe- cto re- sur- re- cti- o- nem mor- tu- o-
-nem pec- ca- to- rum. Et ex- spe- cto re- sur- re- cti- o- nem mor- tu- o-
pec- ca- to- rum. Et ex- spe- cto re- sur- re- cti- o- nem mor- tu- o-
-nem pec- ca- to- rum. Et ex- spe- cto re- sur- re- cti- o- nem mor- tu- o-
-rum. Et vi- tam ven- tu- ri sae- cu- li. A- men.
-rum. Et vi- tam ven- tu- ri sae- cu- li, ven- tu- ri sae- cu- li. A- men.
-rum. Et vi- tam ven- tu- ri sae- cu- li, ven- tu- ri sae- cu- li. A- men.
-rum. Et vi- tam ven- tu- ri sae- cu- li. A- men.
Sanctus
San- - - - ctus,
San- - ctus, San- -
San- - - ctus, San- -
San- ctus, San- - ctus, San-

10
San- - ctus Do- mi- nus De- us Sa-
-ctus, San- - ctus, San- ctus, San-
-ctus, San- - ctus, San- ctus, San- -
-ctus, San- ctus, San- - - ctus, San-
15
- ba- oth, Do- - mi- nus De- us Sa- ba- oth,
- ctus, San- ctus Do- mi- nus De- - us Sa- ba- oth, Do-
- ctus Do- mi- nus De- us Sa- ba- oth, Do- mi-
- ctus Do- - mi- nus
20
Do- - mi- nus De- us Sa- ba- oth, Do- mi- nus De- us Sa- ba- oth.
- - mi- nus De- us, Do- mi- nus De- us Sa- ba- oth.
-nus De- - us Sa- - ba- oth.
De- us Sa- - ba- oth, Sa- - ba- oth.
25
Ple- - ni sunt cae- li et ter-
Ple- ni sunt cae- li et
Ple- ni sunt cae- - li et ter-
Ple- ni sunt cae- li et ter-

30
- ra glo- ri- a tu- a, glo- ri-
ter- ra glo- ri- a tu- a, glo- ri- a tu- - a,
- ra glo- ri- a, glo- - ri- a tu- a,
- ra glo- ri- a tu-
35
-a tu- a.
glo- ri- a tu- a, glo- - ri- a tu- a.
glo- ri- a tu- a, glo- ri- a tu- a.
-a, glo- ri- a tu- a, glo- ri- a tu- a.
40
Be- ne- di- - ctus,
Be- ne- di- - ctus qui ve- nit, qui ve-
Be- ne- di- ctus, Be- ne- di-
45
Be- ne- di- ctus qui ve- - nit, qui ve-
- - nit, qui ve- nit, qui ve- - nit
- ctus qui ve- nit, qui ve-

50
- nit in no- mi- ne, in
in no- mi- ne, in no-mi- ne Do- mi- ni,
-nit in no- mi- ne, in no- mi- ne, in no-
55
no- mi- ne Do- mi- ni, Do- - mi- ni.
in no- mi- ne, in no- mi- ne Do- mi- ni.
-mi- ne Do- mi- ni.
60
Ho- san- na in ex- cel- sis, Ho- san- na in ex- cel- sis, Ho-
Ho- san- na in ex- cel- - sis, Ho- san- na
Ho- san- na in ex- cel- sis, in ex- cel- sis, Ho- san- na in
Ho- san- - na in ex- cel- sis, in ex- cel- sis, in
65
-san- na, Ho- san- na in ex- cel- - sis.
in ex- cel- sis, Ho- san- - na, [Ho- san- na] in ex- cel- sis.
ex- cel- sis, in ex- cel- sis, Ho- san- na, Ho- san- na in ex- cel- sis.
ex- cel- sis, Ho- san- na, Ho- san- na in ex- cel- sis, in ex- cel- sis.

Agnus Dei

A- gnus De- i, A- gnus De-
A- gnus De- i, [De- - i,] A- gnus De-
A- gnus De- i, A- gnus De- i,
A- gnus De- i, A- - gnus De-
5
-i, A- - gnus De- i, A- - gnus De- i,
-i, A- gnus De- i, A- gnus De- i, A- gnus De- i, qui
A- gnus De- i, A- - gnus De- i, qui tol- lis
-i, A- gnus De- i, A- gnus De- i, A- gnus
10
qui tol- lis pec- ca- ta mun- di, pec- ca- ta mun- di: mi-
tol- lis pec- - ca- ta mun- di, qui tol- lis pec- ca- ta mun- di: mi- se- re- re
pec- ca- ta mun- di, pec-ca-ta mun- di, pec-ca- ta mun- di: mi- se- re- re
De- i, qui tol- lis pec- ca- ta mun- di: mi- se- re- re
15
- se- re- - re no- - bis.
no- bis, mi- se- re- re no- bis, mi- se- re- - re no- bis.
no- bis, mi- se- re- re no- bis, mi- se- re- re no- bis.
no- bis, mi- se- re- re no- bis, mi- se- re- re no- bis.

Missa Si du malheur

Kyrie

15
-ste e- lei- son. Ky- ri- e e- lei- son, Ky-
-son. Ky- ri- e e- lei-
e- lei- son. Ky- ri- e e- lei- son, Ky-
e- lei- son. Ky- ri- e e- lei- son, Ky-
20
-ri- e e- lei- son, [Ky- ri- e e- lei- son.]
-son, Ky- ri- e e- lei- son, Ky- ri- e e- lei- son.
-ri- e e- lei- son, e- - lei- son.
-ri- e e- lei- son, Ky- - ri- e e- lei- son.

Gloria

Et in ter- ra pax ho- mi- ni- bus bo- nae vo- lun- ta- tis. Lau-
Et in ter- ra pax ho- mi- ni-bus, ho- mi- ni- bus bo- nae vo- - lun- ta- tis. Lau-
Et in ter- ra pax ho- mi- ni- bus bo- nae vo- lun- ta- tis. Lau-
Et in ter- ra pax ho- mi- ni- bus bo- nae vo- lun- ta- tis.
5
-da- mus te. Be- ne- di- ci- mus te. Ad- o- ra- mus te. Glo- ri- fi-
-da- mus te. Be- ne- di- ci- mus te. Ad- o- ra - mus te. Glo- ri- fi- ca- mus
-da- mus te. Be- ne- di- ci- mus te. Ad- o- ra- mus te. Glo- ri- fi- ca-
Be- ne- di- ci- mus te. Ad- o- ra- mus te. Glo- ri- fi- ca-

-ca- mus te. Gra- ti- as a- gi- mus ti- bi pro- pter
te, glo- ri- fi- ca- mus te. Gra- - ti- as a- gi- mus ti- bi pro- pter ma-
- - mus te. Gra- - ti- as a- gi- mus ti- bi pro- pter
- mus te. Gra- - ti- as a- gi- mus ti- bi pro- pter
ma- gnam glo- ri- am tu- am. Do- mi- ne De- us, Do- mi- ne De-
- gnam glo- ri- am tu- - am. Do- mi- ne De- us, Rex cae- le-
ma- gnam glo- ri- am tu- am. Do- mi- ne De- us, Rex cae-
ma- gnam glo- ri- am tu- am. Do- mi- ne De- us, Rex cae- le-
-us, Rex cae- le- stis, De- us Pa- ter o- mni- po- tens.
-stis, De- us Pa- ter, De- us Pa- ter o- mni- po- tens. Do-
- le- stis, De- - us Pa- ter, De- us Pa- ter o- mni- - po- tens.
- stis, De- us Pa- ter o- mni- po- tens.
Do- mi- ne Fi- li u- ni- ge- ni- te Je- su Chri- ste. Do-
-mi- ne Fi- li u- ni- ge- ni- te, u- ni- ge- ni- te Je- su Chri- - ste.
Do- mi- ne Fi- li u- ni- ge- ni- te Je- su Chri- ste. Do- mi- ne De-
Do- mi- ne Fi- li u- ni- ge- ni- te Je- su Chri- ste. Do-

30
-mi- ne De- us, A- - gnus De- i, Fi- - li-us Pa- tris.
Do- mi- ne De- us, A- gnus De- i, Fi- li- us Pa- tris.
-us, A- - gnus De- i, Fi- - li- us Pa- tris.
-mi- ne De- us, A- gnus De- i, Fi- - li- us Pa- tris.
35
Qui tol- lis pec- ca- ta mun- di, mi- se- re- re no-
Qui tol- lis pec- ca- ta mun- di, mi-
Qui tol- lis pec- ca- ta mun- di, mi- se- re- re
Qui tol- lis pec- ca- ta mun- di, mi- se- re- re no-
-bis. Qui tol- lis pec- ca- - ta mun-
- se- re- re no- bis. Qui tol- lis pe- ca- -
no- - bis. Qui tol- lis pec- ca- ta mun- di,
-bis, mi- se- re- re no- bis. Qui
40
- di, sus- - ci- pe de- - pre-ca- ti- o- nem no- stram.
-ta mun- di, pec- ca- - ta mun- di, sus- - ci- pe de- - pre-ca- ti- o- nem no- stram. Qui
qui tol- lis pec-ca- ta mun- di, sus- ci- pe de- pre- ca- ti- o- nem no- stram. Qui
tol- lis pec- ca- ta mun- di, sus- - ci- pe de- - pre-ca- ti- o- nem no- stram.

45
Qui se- des ad dex- te- ram Pa- tris, mi- se- re- re no-
se- des ad dex- te- ram Pa- tris,mi- se- re- re, mi- se- re- re
se- des ad dex- te- ram Pa- tris, mi- se- re- re no-
Qui se- des ad dex- te- ram Pa- tris, mi- se- re- re no- bis.
50
- bis. Quo- - ni- am tu so- lus san- ctus. Tu so- lus Do- mi- nus.Tu so- lus Al-
no- bis. Quo- - ni- am tu so- lus san- ctus. Tu so- lus Do- mi-nus.Tu so- lus Al-
-bis. Quo- ni- am tu so- lus san- ctus. Tu so- lus Do- mi-nus.Tu so- lus Al-
Quo- - ni- am tu so- lus san- ctus. Tu so- lus Do- mi- nus.Tu so- lus Al-
55
-tis- si- mus, Je- su Chri- ste. Cum San- - cto Spi- - ri-
-tis- si- mus, Je- su Chri- ste. Cum San- cto Spi- ri- tu,
-tis- si- mus, Je- su Chri- ste. Cum San- cto Spi- ri- tu,
-tis- si- mus, Je- su Chri- ste. Cum San- cto Spi- ri- tu,
60
-tu, in glo- - ri- a De- i Pa- tris. A- - men.
in glo- - ri- a De- i Pa- tris. A- - men.
in glo- - ri- a De- i Pa- - tris. A- - men.
in glo- ri- a De- i Pa- - tris. A- men.

Credo

Pa- - trem o- mni- po- ten- tem, fa- cto- rem cae- li et ter-
Pa- trem o- mni- po- ten- tem, fa- cto- rem cae- li et ter-
Pa- trem o- mni- po- ten- tem, fa- cto- rem cae- li et ter-
Pa- trem o- mni- po- ten- - tem, fa- cto- rem
- rae, vi- si- bi- li- um o- mni- um et
-rae, fa- cto- rem cae- li et ter- rae, vi- - si- bi- li- um o- mni-
-rae, fa- cto- rem cae- li et ter- rae, vi- si- bi- li- um o- mni-
cae- li et- ter- rae, vi- si- bi- li- um o- mni- um
in- vi- si- bi- - li- um. Et in u- num Do- mi- num Je- sum
-um et in- vi- si- bi- - li- um. Et in u- num Do- mi- num Je- sum
-um et in- vi- si- bi- - li- um. Et in u- num Do-mi- num Je-
et in- vi- si- bi- - li- um. Et in u- num Do- mi- num Je- sum
Chri- stum, Fi- li- um De- i u- - ni- ge- ni- tum. Et ex Pa- tre na-
Chri- stum, Fi- li- um De- i u- - ni- ge- ni- tum. Et ex Pa- tre na-
-sum Chri- stum, Fi- li- um De- i u- ni- ge- ni- tum. Et ex Pa- tre na-
Chri- stum, u- - ni- ge- ni- tum. Et ex Pa- tre na-

20
-tum an- te o- mni- a sae- cu- la. De-
-tum an- te o- mni- a sae- cu-la. De- - um de De- o, lu- men de
-tum an- te o- mni- a sae- cu- la. De- um de De- o, lu-
-tum an- te o- mni- a sae- cu- la. De- - um de De-
25
- um de De- o, lu- men de lu- - mi- ne, De- um ve- rum
lu- mi- ne, De- um ve- - rum de De- o ve-
- men de lu- - mi- ne, De- um ve- rum de De- o ve- ro, De-um ve-
-o, lu- - men de lu- mi- ne, De- um ve- rum
30
de De- o ve- - ro. Ge- ni- tum, non fa- ctum,
-ro, de De- o ve- ro. Ge- ni- tum, non fa- ctum, con- sub- stan-
-rum de De- o ve- ro. Ge- ni- tum, non fa- ctum, con- sub- stan- ti- a-
de De- o ve- ro. con- sub-stan- ti-
35
con- sub- stan- ti- a- lem Pa- tri: per quem o- mni- a fa- cta
-ti- a- lem Pa- tri: per quem o- mni-a fa- cta sunt, per quem o-
-lem Pa- tri: per quem o-mni- a fa- cta sunt, per quem o- mni- a fa- cta
-a- lem Pa- tri: per quem o- mni- a fa- cta

sunt, o- mni-a fa- cta sunt. Qui pro- pter nos ho- mi-
- mni-a fa- - cta sunt. Qui pro- pter nos ho- mi- nes, et
sunt, o- - mni- a fa- cta sunt. Qui pro- pter nos ho- mi- nes, et
sunt, o- - mni- a fa- cta sunt. Qui pro- pter nos ho- mi- nes,
40
-nes, et pro- pter no- stram sa- - lu- tem de- scen- - dit
pro- pter no-stram sa- lu- tem de- scen- - dit de cae- lis, de- scen-
pro- pter, et pro- pter no- stram sa- lu- tem de- scen- dit de cae-
et pro- pter no- stram sa- lu- tem de- scen- dit
45
de cae- lis. Et in- car- na- tus est de
- dit de cae- lis. Et in- car- na- - tus est
- lis. Et in- car- na- - tus est de
de cae- lis. Et in- car- na- - tus est
50
Spi- ri- tu San- - cto ex Ma- ri- a Vir- gi-
de Spi- - ri- tu San- - cto ex Ma- ri- - a Vir- gi-
Spi- ri- tu San- - cto ex Ma- ri- - a Vir- gi-
de Spi- ri- tu San- - cto ex Ma- ri- - a Vir- gi-
55

-ne: Et ho-mo fa - - ctus est.
-ne: Et ho- mo fa - ctus est.
-ne: Et ho-mo fa - - ctus est. Cru - - ci-fi-xus e -
-ne: Et ho - mo fa - ctus est. Cru - ci - fi - xus e - ti -
sub Pon ti - o Pi - la - - to
sub Pon-ti - o Pi - la - to pas-
- ti- am pro no - bis: sub Pon-ti - o Pi - la - - to
- am pro no - - bis: sub Pon-ti - o Pi - la - to
pas - sus, et se - pul - tus est. Et
- sus, et se - pul - tus est, et se - pul - tus est. Et
pas - sus, et se - - pul - tus est. Et
pas - - sus, et se - pul - tus est. Et
re - sur - re - xit ter - ti - a di - e, se - cun - dum Scri - ptu - ras. Et a - scen-dit in cae-lum:
re - sur - re - xit ter - ti - a di - e, se - cun - dum Scri-ptu - ras. Et a - scen-dit in cae-lum:
re - sur - re - xit ter - ti - a di - e, se - cun - dum Scri - ptu - ras. Et a - scen-dit in cae-lum:
re - sur - re - xit ter - ti - a di - e, Et a - scen-dit in cae-lum:

75
se - det ad dex - te - ram Pa - tris. Et i - te-rum ven-tu - rus est cum glo - ri - a,
se - det ad dex - te-ram Pa - tris. Et i - te-rum ven-tu-rus est cum glo - ri - a,
se - det ad dex-te - ram Pa - tris. ven-tu-rus est cum glo - ri - a,
se - det ad dex - te - ram Pa - tris. ven-tu-rus est cum glo - ri - a,
80
ju - di - ca - re vi - vos et mor - tu - os: cu - jus re - gni
ju - di - ca - re vi - vos et mor - tu - os: cu - jus re - gni non
ju - di - ca - re vi - vos et mor - tu - os: cu - jus re - gni, cu - jus re -
ju - di - ca - re vi - vos et mor - tu - os: cu - jus re - gni non e -
85
non e - rit fi - nis. San -
e - rit fi - nis. Et in Spi - ri - tum San -
gni non e - rit fi - nis. Et in Spi - ri - tum San -
rit fi - nis. Et in Spi - ri - tum San -
90
ctum, Do - mi - num, et vi - vi - fi - can - tem: qui ex Pa - tre, Fi - li -
ctum, Do - mi - num, et vi - vi - fi - can - tem: qui ex Pa - tre, Fi - li - o -
ctum, Do - mi - num, et vi - vi - fi - can - tem: qui ex Pa - tre, Fi - li -
ctum, Do - mi - num, et vi - vi - fi - can - tem: qui ex Pa - tre, Fi - li - o -

95
-o-que pro-ce-dit. Qui cum Pa-tre et Fi-li-o si-mul ad-o-ra-tur, et
-que pro-ce-dit. Qui cum Pa-tre et Fi-li-o si-mul ad-o-ra-tur, et
-o-que pro-ce-dit. Qui cum Pa-tre et Fi-li-o si-mul ad-o-ra-tur, et
-que pro-ce-dit. et Fi-li-o si-mul ad-o-ra-tur, et
100
con-glo-ri-fi-ca-tur: qui lo-cu-tus est per Pro-phe-tas. Et
con-glo-ri-fi-ca-tur: qui lo-cu-tus est per Pro-phe-tas. Et
con-glo-ri-fi-ca-tur: qui lo-cu-tus est per Pro-phe-tas. Et
con-glo-ri-fi-ca-tur: qui lo-cu-tus est per Pro-phe-tas. Et
u-nam san-ctam ca-tho-li-cam et a-po-sto-li-cam Ec-
u-nam san-ctam ca-tho-li-cam et a-po-sto-li-cam Ec-
u-nam san-ctam ca-tho-li-cam et a-po-sto-li-cam
u-nam san-ctam ca-tho-li-cam et a-po-sto-li-cam Ec-
105
-cle-si-am. Con-fi-te-or u-num ba-pti-sma
-cle-si-am. Con-fi-te-or u-num ba-pti-sma
Ec-cle-si-am. Con-fi-te-or u-num ba-pti-sma
-cle-si-am. Con-fi-te-or u-num ba-pti-sma

in re - mis - si - o - nem pec - - ca - to - - rum. re - sur - re - cti - o - - nem mor - - tu - o - rum. Et vi - tam ven - tu - ri sae - - cu - li. A - men.
in re - mis - si - o - nem pec - ca - to - rum. Et ex - - spe - - cto re - - sur - re - cti - o - nem mor - - tu - o - rum. Et vi - tam ven - tu - ri sae - cu - li. A - men.
in re - mis - si - - o - nem pec - ca - to - - rum. Et ex - spe - - cto re - - sur - re - cti - o - - nem mor - - tu - o - rum. Et vi - tam ven - tu - ri sae - cu - li. A - men.
in re - mis - si - o - nem pec - ca - to - rum. Et ex - spe - - cto re - sur - re - cti - o - nem mor - - tu - o - rum. Et vi - tam ven - tu - ri sae - cu - li. A - men.

Sanctus

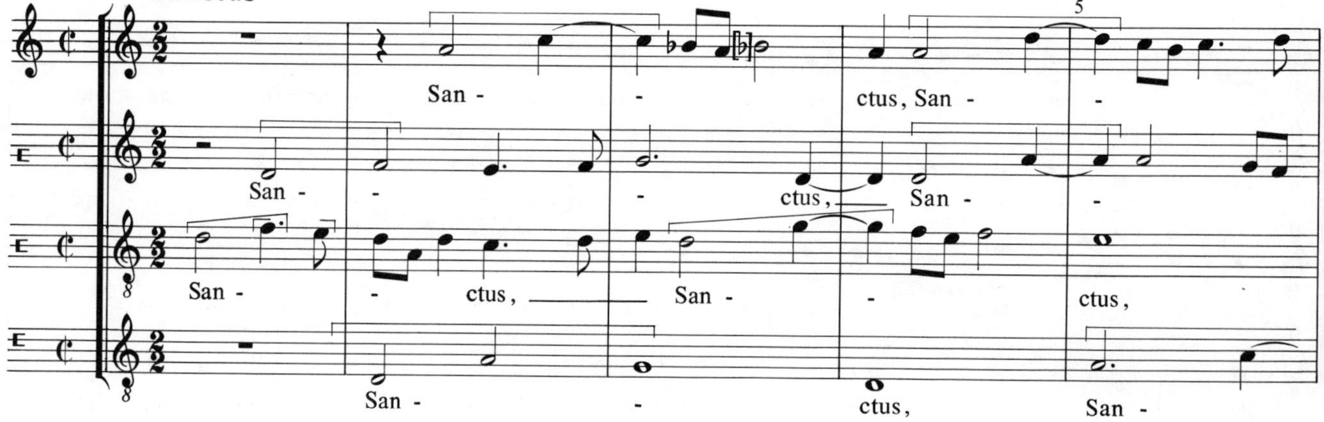
San - - ctus, San - -
San - - - ctus, San - -
San - - ctus, San - - ctus,
San - - ctus, San -

10
- - ctus Do - mi - nus De -
- ctus, San - ctus Do - - mi - nus De - us Sa - ba - oth, Do -
San - - ctus, San - ctus Do - mi -
- ctus Do - mi - nus De - us Sa - ba -
15
- us Sa - ba - oth, Do - mi - nus De - us Sa - ba - oth. Ple -
- mi - nus De - us, Do - - mi - nus De - us Sa - - ba-
- nus De - - us Sa - ba - oth, Sa - ba - oth. Ple -
- oth, Do - mi - nus De - us Sa - - ba - oth.
20
- ni sunt cae - li et ter - ra, et ter - ra, ple - ni sunt cae - li et ter -
- oth. Ple- ni sunt cae - li et ter - ra, ple - ni sunt cae - li et ter -
- ni sunt cae - li, ple - ni sunt cae - li et ter - ra glo -
Ple - ni sunt cae - li et ter - ra, ple -
25
- ra glo - ri - a tu - a.
- ra, et ter - ra glo - - ri - a tu - a.
- ri - a tu - a, glo - ri - a tu - a, glo - - ri - a tu - a.
- ni sunt cae - - li et ter - ra glo - ri - a tu - a.

30
Be - ne - di - ctus qui ve - nit, qui
Be - ne - di - ctus qui
35
ve - nit, qui ve - nit in no -
ve - nit, qui ve - nit in no - mi - ne
qui ve - nit in no - mi - ne,
40
- mi - ne Do - mi - ni, in no - mi - ne,
Do - mi - ni, in no - mi - ne
in no - mi - ne Do -
45
in no - mi - ne, in no - mi - ne Do - mi - ni.
Do - mi - ni, in no - mi - ne Do - mi - ni.
- mi - ni, in no - mi - ne Do - mi - ni.

Agnus Dei

* The source gives no time signature here.

5
- i, qui tol - lis pec - ca - - ta mun - di, qui tol - lis pec - ca - ta mun -
qui tol - lis pec - ca - ta mun - di, qui tol - lis pec - ca - ta mun - di:
qui tol - lis, qui tol - lis pec - ca - ta mun - di, qui tol - lis pec - ca -
qui tol - lis pec - ca - ta mun - di, qui tol - lis pec - ca - ta mun-
10
- di, pec - ca - ta mun - di: mi - se - re - re, mi - se - re -
mi - - se - re - re no - - bis, mi - se - re - re
- ta mun - - di: mi - - se - re - re no - bis, mi - se - re -
- di, pec - ca - ta mun di: mi - se - re -
15
- re no - bis, mi - se - re - - re no - bis.
no - bis, mi - se - re - re no - bis, mi - se - re - re no - bis.
- re no - bis, mi - se - re - re no - bis.
- re no - bis, mi - se - re - re no - bis.

Missa Super ripam Jordanis

Kyrie

15
-lei - son, Ky - ri - e e - lei - son,
- son, Ky - ri - e e - lei - son, Ky - ri - e e-
- e e - lei - son,] Ky - ri - e e - lei - son, Ky - ri - e
- ri - e e - lei - son, Ky - ri - e e-
Ky - ri - e e - lei - son, Ky - ri - e
20
Ky - ri - e e - lei - son. Chri - ste e - lei - son, Chri - ste
- lei - son. Chri - ste e - lei - son, Chri - ste e - lei -
e - lei - son. Chri - ste e -
- lei - son, [e - lei - son.]
e - lei - son, e - lei - son.
25
e - lei - son, Chri -
- son, Chri - ste e - lei -
- lei - son, Chri - ste e - lei -
Chri - ste e - lei - son, Chri -
Chri - ste e - lei - son, Chri - ste e - lei -

30
- ste e - lei - - son, Chri - ste e - lei - son, Chri -
- son, Chri - ste e - lei - - son, Chri -
- son, Chri - ste e - lei - son, e - lei - son,
- ste e - lei - son, Chri - - ste e - lei - -
- son, Chri - ste e - - lei - son, [Chri - ste e -
35
- ste e - - lei - son.
- ste e - - lei - son, Chri - ste e - lei - son.
Chri - ste e - lei - son, [e - le - i - son.]
- son, e - lei - son, Chri - ste e - lei - son.
- lei - son,] Chri - ste e - lei - son, e - lei - son.
40
Ky - - ri - e e - - lei - son, Ky - ri - e e - lei -
Ky - ri - e e - - lei - son, Ky - ri -
Ky - ri - e e - - lei - son,
Ky - - ri - e e - lei -
Ky - ri - e e - lei -

45
- son, Ky - - ri - e
- e e - lei - son, [Ky- ri - e e - lei - son,] Ky -
Ky - - ri - e e - lei - - son, Ky - rie e -
- son, Ky - ri - e e - lei - son, Ky - - ri - e e - lei -
- son, Ky - ri - e e - lei - son, Ky - rie e -
50
e - lei - - son,
- ri - e e - - lei - son, Ky - ri - e e -
- lei - son, Ky - ri - e e - -
- son, Ky - ri - e e - lei -
- lei - son, Ky - - ri - e e - lei -
55
Ky - - ri - e e - lei - - son.
- lei - son.
- lei - son, Ky - ri - e e - lei - son.
- son, Ky - ri - e e - lei - - son.
- son, Ky - ri - e e - lei - son.

Gloria

Et in ter - - ra pax ho - mi - ni-bus, ho - - - mi - ni -
Et in ter - ra pax ho - mi - ni - bus bo-nae vo -
Et in ter - ra pax ho-mi - ni -
- bus bo - nae vo-lun - ta - tis. Lau-da - - mus te, lau - da -
- lun-ta - - - tis. Lau-da - mus te. Be -
- bus bo-nae vo - lun - ta - - tis. Be - ne -
bo - nae vo - - lun-ta - tis. Lau-da - mus te. Be -
bo - nae vo - - lun-ta - tis. Lau -
- mus te. Be - ne - di - ci-mus te. Ad - o - ra - mus te. Glo -
- ne - di - ci - mus te. Ad - o - ra - mus te.
- di - ci - mus te. Ad - o - ra - - mus [te.] Glo -
- ne - di - ci - mus te. Ad - o - ra - mus te. Glo - ri - fi -
- da - mus te. Be - ne - di - ci - mus te. Glo - ri - fi -

20
- ri - fi - ca - mus te, glo - ri - fi - ca - mus te. Gra - - ti - as a -
Glo - ri - fi - ca - - mus te. Gra - ti - as a -
- ri - fi - ca - mus te, glo - ri - fi - ca - mus te. Gra - - ti - as a - gi -
- ca - mus te, glo - ri - fi - ca - mus te. Gra - ti - as
- ca - mus te. Gra - - ti - as a -
25
- gi - mus ti - bi pro - - pter ma - gnam, pro - pter
- gi - mus ti - - bi pro - pter ma - gnam glo - - ri - am tu -
- mus ti - bi pro - - pter ma - gnam glo - ri - am tu - am,
a - gi - mus ti - bi pro - pter ma -
- gi - mus ti - bi pro - pter ma - gnam glo - ri - am tu -
30
ma - gnam glo - ri - am tu - am. Do - - mi - ne De - us,
- am, ma - - gnam glo - ri am tu - am. Do - - mi - ne
pro - pter ma - - gnam glo - ri - am tu - - am. Do -
- gnam glo - ri - am tu - am. Do - mi - ne De - us, Rex cae - le - stis, Do -
- - am. Do - mi - ne De - us, Rex cae - le -

35
Rex cae-le - - stis, De - - us Pa - ter o -
De - us, Rex cae - le - stis, De - us Pa - ter o - mni -
- mi - ne De - us, Rex cae - le - stis, De - us Pa - ter o -
- mi - ne De - us, Rex cae - le - stis, De - us Pa - ter o - mni - po - tens.
- stis, Rex cae - le - stis, De - us Pa - ter o -
40
- mni - po - tens. Do - mi - ne Fi - li u - ni - ge - ni - te
- po - tens. Do - mi - ne Fi - li u - ni - ge - ni - te Je - su
- mni - po - tens. Do - mi - ne Fi - li u - - ni - ge - ni - te Je - su Chri - ste,
Do - mi - ne Fi - li, Do - mi - ne Fi - li u - ni - ge - ni - te
- mni - po - tens. Do - mi - ne Fi - li Je - su
45
Je - su Chri - - ste, Je - - su Chri -
Chri - ste, Je - su Chri - ste, Je - su Chri - ste, Je -
Je - su Chri - - ste, Je - su Chri - ste. Do -
Je - - su Chri - ste. Do - mi - ne De - - us,
Chri - ste, Je - su Chri - ste. Do - mi - ne De - us, A -

50
55
60
- ste, Je - su Chri - ste. Do - mi - ne De - us, A -
- su Chri - ste. Do - - mi - ne De - us, A - - gnus De -
- mi - ne De - - us, A - gnus De - i, Do - mi - ne De - us, A - gnus De -
A - gnus De - i, A - gnus De - i, A - gnus De -
- gnus De - i, A - gnus De - i, A - gnus De - i,
- gnus De - i, Fi - li - us Pa - - tris, Fi -
- i, Fi - li - us Pa - tris, Fi - li - us Pa -
- i, Fi - li - us Pa - tris, Fi - li - us Pa -
- i, Fi - li - us Pa - tris,
Fi - li - us Pa - tris, Fi - li - us Pa - tris, Fi - - li - us
- li - us Pa - - tris, Fi - li - us Pa - tris, Fi - - li - us Pa - - tris.
- tris, Fi - li - us Pa - - tris.
- tris, Fi - li - us Pa - tris, Fi - li - us Pa - tris.
Fi - li - us Pa - tris, Fi - - li - us Pa - tris.
Pa - tris, Fi - li - us Pa - tris, Fi - li - us Pa - tris.

65
Qui tol - lis pec - ca - ta mun - di, qui tol - lis pec-
Qui tol - lis pec- ca - ta mun - di, pec - ca - - ta mun -
Qui tol - lis pec - ca - ta mun - di, pec -
Qui tol -
Qui tol - lis pec - ca - ta mun -
70
- ca - ta mun- di, mi - se - re - re no - bis.
- di, mi - se - - re - - re no - bis. Qui tol - lis
- ca - ta mun - di, mi - se - re - re no - bis, mi - se - re - re no -
- lis pec - ca - ta mun - di, Qui tol - lis pec - ca -
- di, mi - se - re - re no - bis. Qui tol - lis pec - ca - ta
75
Qui tol - lis pec - ca - ta mun - di, sus - - ci pe, sus -
pec - ca - ta mun - di, pec - ca - ta mun - di, sus - ci -
- bis. Qui tol - lis pec - ca - ta mun - di, sus - ci -
- ta mun - di, qui tol - lis pec - ca - ta mun - di, sus - ci -
mun - - di, sus - - ci -

80
- ci - pe de - pre - ca - ti - o - nem
- pe, sus - - ci - pe de - pre - ca - ti - o - nem no - stram,
- pe de - - pre - ca - ti - o - nem, de - pre - ca - ti - o - nem no - stram,
- pe, sus - - ci - pe de - - pre - ca - ti - o - nem no - stram, de -
- pe de - - pre - ca - ti - o - nem no - stram.
85
no - stram. Qui se - - des ad dex - te - ram Pa - tris, mi -
de - pre - ca - ti - o - nem no - stram. Qui se - des ad dex - te -
[de - pre - ca - ti - o - nem no - stram.] Qui se - des ad dex - te - ram
- pre - ca - ti - o - nem no - - stram.
Qui se - des ad dex - te - ram Pa - tris,
90
- se - re - re no - bis, mi - se - re - re no - bis, mi - se - re -
- ram Pa - tris, mi - se - re - re no - bis, mi - se - re -
Pa - tris, mi - se - re - re, mi - se - re - re no - bis,
mi - se - re - re no - bis, mi - se - re - re no - bis,
mi - se - re - re no - bis, mi - se -

95
-re no-bis. Quo- - ni-am tu so- lus san- ctus.
-re no - - bis. Quo - ni-am tu so - lus san-ctus.
mi - se-re-re no - bis. Quo- - ni-am tu
mi-se-re - re no-bis. Quo - ni-am tu so - lus san- ctus.
-re-re no - - bis. Tu so - lus
100
Tu so - lus Al-tis - si - mus, tu so -
Tu so - lus Do - - mi-nus. Tu so - lus Al-tis - si -
so - lus san- ctus. Tu so - lus Do-mi-nus. Tu so -
Tu so - lus Al - tis-si-mus, Al-tis-si - mus, Tu
Do-mi-nus, tu so-lus Do - mi - nus. Tu so - lus Al-tis-si - mus, Je-su
105
-lus Al - tis - - si - mus, Je - su Chri - - ste.
-mus, Je - - su Chri - ste, Je - su
-lus Al - tis - - si - mus, Je - su Chri- - ste. Cum
so - lus Al - tis - si - mus, Je - su Chri - ste. Cum
Chri - ste, Je - su Chri - - ste.

110
Cum San-cto Spi - ri - tu, cum San-cto Spi-ri - tu,
Chri - ste. Cum San - cto Spi - ri - tu, cum San-cto Spi - ri - tu,
San-cto Spi - - ri tu, cum San-cto Spi - - ri tu,
San - cto Spi - ri - tu, cum San-cto Spi - ri - tu,
Cum San-cto Spi - - ri - tu, in
115
in glo - ri - a De - i, in glo- - ri - a De - i,
in glo - ri - a De - i, in glo - ri - a De - i, in glo - ri - a De - i,
in glo - ri - a De - i Pa - tris, in
in glo - ri - a De - i, in glo - ri - a De - i, in glo - ri -
glo - ri - a De - i, cum San-cto Spi - ri - tu, in glo - ri -
120
in glo - ri - a De - i Pa - tris. A - men, in glo - ri - a De - i Pa -
in glo - - ri - a De - i
glo - ri - a De - i Pa - tris, in glo - ri - a, in glo - ri - a
- a De - i, in glo - ri - a De - i Pa - tris. A - men, in glo - ri - a
- a De - i Pa - tris. A - men, in glo - - ri - a

125
-tris. A - men, a - men, De - i Pa - tris. A - men.
Pa - tris. A - - men.
De - i Pa - tris. A - men, in glo - ri - a De - i Pa - tris. A - men.
De - i Pa - - tris. A - men.
De - i Pa - tris. A - men, De - i Pa - tris. A - men.
Credo
5
Pa - trem o - mni - po - ten - - tem, o -
Pa - trem o - mni - po - ten - tem, o - mni -
Pa - trem o - mni - po - ten - tem, fa - cto - rem cae - li et
Pa - trem o - mni - po -
10
- mni - po - - ten - tem, vi - si - bi -
- po - ten - tem, fa - cto - rem cae - - li et ter - rae, vi -
ter - rae, fa - - cto - rem cae - li et ter - -
fa - cto - rem cae - li et ter - rae, fa - cto - rem cae - li et ter -
- ten - tem, fa - cto - rem cae - li et ter - rae,

- li - um o - mni - um et in - vi - si - bi - li - um. Et in
- si - bi - li - um o - mni - um et in - vi - si - bi -
- rae, et in - vi - si - bi - li - um. Et in u -
- rae, et in - vi - - si - bi - li - um.
vi - si - bi - li - um o - - mni - um
15
u - num Do - mi - num Je - sum Chri - stum,
- li - um. Et in u - num Do - mi - num Je - sum
- num Do mi - num Je - sum Chri - stum, Je - sum Chri - stum, Fi -
Et in u - num Do - - - mi - num Je - - sum Chri -
Et in u - - num Do - mi - num Je - sum Chri - stum,
20
Fi - li - um De - i u - ni - ge - ni - tum. Et ex Pa -
Chri - stum, Fi - li - um De - i u - ni - ge - ni - tum.
- li - um De - - i u - - ni - ge - ni - tum.
- stum, Fi - li - um De - i u - ni - ge - ni - tum. Et ex Pa - tre
Fi - li - um De - i u - ni - ge - ni - tum. Et ex

25
-tre na-tum an- te o-mni-a sae- cu- la. De-um de De-
an- te o-mni-a sae-cu- la. De- - um de De- o, lu-
an- - te o-mni- a sae-cu-la. De- um de De-
na- tum an- - te o mni- a sae-cu- la. De-um
Pa-tre na- tum an-te o- mni- a sae-cu- la. De- um de De-
30
- o, lu- men de lu-mi-ne, De- - um
- men de lu- mi- ne, De-um ve- - rum, De- um ve-
- o, lu-men de lu- mi- ne, lu-men de lu-mi-ne, De- - um ve-
de De- - o, lu- men de lu-mi-ne, De- um ve- rum,
- o, lu-men de lu- mi- ne, De- - um ve-
35
ve- rum de De-o ve- - ro. Ge- ni-tum, non fa-ctum, con-
- rum de De-o ve- ro, de De-o ve- ro. Ge-
- rum de De- o ve- ro, De- um ve- rum de De-o ve-ro.
De- um ve-rum de De- o ve- ro. Ge-
- rum de De- o ve- ro. Ge- ni-tum, non fa-ctum,

40
- sub - stan - ti - a - lem Pa - tri: per quem o - mni - a fa -
- ni - tum, non fa - ctum, per quem o - mni - a fa -
con - - sub - stan - ti - a - lem Pa - tri: per quem o - mni - a
- ni - tum, non fa - ctum, per quem o - mni - a fa - cta
con - sub - stan - ti - a - - lem Pa - tri:
45
- cta sunt. et pro - pter no - stram
- cta sunt. Qui pro - pter nos ho - mi -
fa - cta sunt. Qui pro - pter nos ho - - mi - nes,
sunt. Qui pro - pter nos ho - mi - nes, et
Qui pro - pter nos ho - mi - nes, et pro - pter
50
sa - lu - - tem de - - scen - dit de cae -
- nes, et pro - pter no - stram sa - lu - - tem de - scen - dit de cae - lis,
et pro - pter no - stram sa - lu - tem de - scen-
pro - pter no - stram sa - lu - tem de - scen - dit, de - scen - dit
no - stram sa - lu - tem de - scen - dit de cae - lis, de -

55
- lis, de-scen-dit de cae - lis,
de-scen - dit de cae-lis, de cae - lis, de-scen - dit de cae -
- dit de cae-lis, de cae - lis, de - scen - dit de cae - lis, [de cae -
de cae-lis, de-scen- dit de cae - lis, de - scen-dit de
- scen-dit de cae - lis, de - scen - dit de cae - lis, de-scen - dit de
60
de - - scen - dit de cae - - lis.
- lis.
- lis.]
cae - lis, de-scen-dit de cae - lis.
cae - lis, de-scen-dit de cae - lis.
65
Et in - car - na - tus est
Et in - car - na - tus est de
Et in - car - na - - tus est, et in - car - na - tus est
Et in - car - na - tus est de Spi - ri - tu San -
Et in - car - na - tus est de Spi - - ri - tu San -

70
de Spi- ri- tu San-
Spi - ri - tu, de Spi-ri- tu San - cto, de Spi-ri- tu San-cto,
de Spi - ri - tu San - cto, de
- cto, de Spi-ri-tu San-cto, de Spi-ri- tu San-cto,
- cto, de Spi - - ri - tu San - cto, de Spi -
75
- cto ex Ma - - ri - - a
de Spi - ri - tu San-cto ex Ma - ri - a Vir - gi - ne,
Spi - ri - tu San - - cto ex Ma - ri - a,
de Spi-ri- tu San - cto ex Ma - ri - a
- ri - tu San - cto ex Ma-ri - - a Vir -
80
Vir - - - gi - ne: Et
ex Ma - ri - a Vir - - gi - ne: Et ho - mo
ex Ma-ri - a Vir - gi - ne: Et ho - mo
Vir - - gi-ne: Et ho - mo fa - ctus
- gi - ne: Et ho -

85
ho - mo fa - ctus est. Cru-ci-fi-
fa - ctus est, et ho-mo fa-ctus est. Cru- ci-fi-xus e-
fa-ctus est, et ho - mo fa-ctus est. Cru - ci - fi-xus e-
est, et ho - mo fa - ctus est. Cru - ci - fi-xus
- mo fa - - ctus est.
90
-xus e - ti - am pro no - - bis: sub Pon - ti-o Pi-la-
-ti-am pro no - bis, e - ti-am pro no-bis: sub Pon - ti - o Pi-la-to,
- ti-am pro no-bis: sub Pon - ti - o, sub Pon-ti - o Pi - la - to
sub Pon - ti - o Pi-la - to pas-
sub Pon - ti-o Pi - la - to, sub Pon-ti-
95
-to pas - sus, et se-pul - - tus est. Et
sub Pon-ti-o Pi-la - to pas - sus, et se-pul-tus est. Et
pas- sus, et se - pul - tus est. Et
- sus, et se - pul-tus est, et se - pul - tus est. Et
- o Pi-la - to pas - sus, et se - pul-tus est. Et

100
re - sur - re - xit ter - ti - a di - e, se - cun - dum Scri - ptu - ras. Et a - scen - dit in cae - lum :
re - sur - re - xit ter - ti - a di - e, se - cun - dum Scri - ptu - ras. Et a - scen - dit in cae - lum :
re - sur - re - xit ter - ti - a di - e, se - cun - dum Scri - ptu - ras. Et a - scen - dit in cae - lum :
re - sur - re - xit ter - ti - a di - e, se - cun - dum Scri - ptu - ras. Et a - scen - dit in cae - lum:
re - sur - re - xit ter - ti - a di - e, se - cun - dum Scri - ptu - ras. Et a - scen - dit in cae - lum :
105
110
se - det ad dex - te - ram Pa - tris, ad dex - te - ram Pa - tris.
se - det ad dex - te - ram Pa - tris, ad dex - te - ram Pa - - tris.
se - det ad dex - te - ram Pa - tris, ad dex - te - ram Pa - tris.
se - det ad dex - te - ram Pa - - tris, ad dex - te - ram Pa - tris.
se - det, se - det ad dex - te - ram Pa - tris.
Et i - te - rum ven - tu - rus est, et i - te - rum ven -
Et i - te - rum ven - - tu - rus est cum glo - ri -
Et i - te - rum ven -

115
- tu - rus est cum glo - ri - a, ju - -
- a, ju - di - ca - re, cum glo - ri - a, ju -
- tu - rus est cum glo - ri - a, ju - di - ca -
120
- di - ca - re vi - -
- di - ca - re vi - - vos et mor - tu -
- re vi - - - vos
125
- vos et mor - tu - os: cu - jus re - - gni, cu -
- os, et mor - - tu - os: cu - jus re - gni non e - rit fi -
et mor - tu - os: cu - jus re - gni non e - rit fi - nis,
130
- jus re - gni non e - rit fi - nis, cu -
- nis, non e - rit fi - nis, cu - - jus re - gni, cu -
cu - jus re - gni non e - - rit fi - nis, cu -

135
- jus re - gni non e - rit fi - - nis.
- jus re - - gni non e - rit fi - - nis.
- jus re - gni non e - rit fi - nis.
140
Et in Spi - ri - tum San - - ctum, Do - mi - num, et
Et in Spi - ri - tum San - - ctum, Do - mi - num,
Et in Spi - ri - tum San - ctum, Do - mi - num,
Et in Spi - ri - tum San - - ctum, Do - - mi - num, et
San - ctum, Do - mi - num, et
145
vi - vi - fi - can - tem: qui ex Pa - tre, Fi - - li - o - que
qui ex Pa - tre, Fi - - li - o - que pro -
et vi - vi - fi - can - tem: qui ex Pa - tre,
vi - vi - fi - can - tem: qui ex Pa - tre, Fi - - li - o - que
vi - vi - fi - can - tem: qui ex Pa - tre, Fi - li -

150
— pro - ce - - dit. si - mul
- ce - dit. — Qui cum Pa - tre et Fi - li - o si -
Qui cum Pa - tre — et Fi - li - o si -
pro - ce - dit. Qui cum Pa - tre et Fi - li - o si -
- o - que pro - ce - dit. Qui — cum Pa - tre et Fi - li - o si -
155
ad - o - ra - - tur, et — con - glo - - ri - fi - ca -
- mul ad - o - ra - tur, et con - glo - ri - fi - ca -
- mul ad - o - ra - tur, et con - glo - ri - - fi - ca -
- mul ad - o - ra - tur, et con - glo - ri - fi - ca - tur: —
- mul ad - o - ra - tur, et con - glo - ri - fi - ca -
160
- tur: qui — lo - cu - tus est, qui lo - cu - tus est per — Pro -
- tur: — qui — lo - cu - tus est per Pro - phe - tas, qui lo -
- tur: qui — lo - cu - tus est per — Pro - phe - tas, qui lo -
— qui lo - cu - - tus est per Pro - phe - tas, qui
- tur: qui — lo - cu - tus est per — Pro - phe - tas,

165
- phe - tas. Et u - nam
- cu - tus est per Pro-phe - tas, per Pro - phe - tas. Et u - nam san-
- cu - tus est per Pro - phe - - tas. Et u - nam
lo - cu - tus est per Pro - phe - - tas. et
qui lo - cu - tus est per Pro-phe - - tas.
san - ctam ca - tho - li - cam et a - po - sto - li - cam, et a - po -
- ctam ca - tho - li - cam et a - po - sto - li - cam, et a - po -
san - ctam ca - tho - li - cam et a - po - sto - li - cam Ec - cle - si -
a - po - sto - li - cam Ec - cle - si - am, Ec -
et a - po - sto - li - cam Ec - cle - si - am, Ec -
170
- sto - li - cam Ec - cle - - si - am. Con - fi - te - or u - num ba - pti - sma, u -
- sto - li - cam Ec - cle - si - am. Con - fi - te - or u - num ba -
- am. Con - fi - te - or u - num ba - pti - sma,
- cle - - si - am. Con - fi - te - or u - num ba - pti - sma, u -
- cle - si - am. Con - fi - te - or u - num ba - pti - sma in re - mis - si -

175
- num ba - pti - sma in re-mis - si - o - nem pec-ca - to - rum.
- pti - sma in re-mis - si - o - nem pec - ca - to - rum. Et
u - num ba - pti - sma in re-mis - si - o - nem pec-ca - to - rum.
- num ba - pti - sma in re-mis - si - o - nem pec-ca - to - rum. Et
- o - nem pec-ca - to - rum. Et ex -
180
185
Et ex - spe - cto re - sur - re - cti - o - nem mor- - tu - o -
ex - spe - cto re - sur - re - cti - o - nem, re - sur - re - cti - o - nem mor - tu - o -
Et ex-spe - cto re - sur - re - cti - o - nem, re - sur - re - cti - o - nem mor - tu - o -
ex - spe - cto re - sur - re - cti - o - nem, re - sur - re - cti - o - nem mor - tu - o -
- spe - cto re - sur - re - cti - o - nem, re - sur - re - cti - o - nem mor - tu - o -
190
- rum. Et vi - tam, et vi -
- rum. Et vi - tam ven - tu - ri, et vi - tam ven -
- rum. Et vi - tam, et vi - tam ven -
- rum. Et vi - tam ven - tu - ri, et vi - tam ven - tu -
- rum. Et vi - tam, et vi - tam

195
- tam ven - tu - ri sae - cu - li. A - - men. Et vi - - tam ven - tu -
- tu - ri sae - cu - li, ven - tu - ri sae - cu - li. A - - men, a - men,
- tu - ri sae - cu - li, ven - tu - ri sae - cu - li, ven - tu - ri
- ri, ven - tu - ri sae - cu - li, ven - tu - ri sae - cu -
ven - tu - ri sae - cu - li. A - men, ven - tu - ri sae - cu -
200
- ri sae - cu - li. A - - men. Et vi - tam ven - tu - ri, ven - tu - ri
ven - tu - ri sae - cu - li, ven - tu - ri
sae - cu - li. A - men, ven - tu - ri sae - cu - li, ven - tu -
- li, ven - tu - ri sae - cu - li. A - men, ven - tu - ri
- li, ven - tu - ri sae - cu - li. A - - men, a - men,
205
sae - cu - li. A - men, sae - cu - li. A - men.
sae - cu - li. A - - men, a - - men.
- ri sae - cu - li, ven - tu - ri sae - cu - li. A - men, a - - men.
sae - cu - li. A - men, a - - men.
ven - tu - ri sae - cu - li, ven - tu - ri sae - cu - li. A - men.

Sanctus

San - - ctus, San - -
San - - ctus, San -
San - -
5
- ctus, San -
- ctus, San - ctus, San - - ctus, San - - ctus
San - - - ctus, San - - ctus
- ctus, San - - ctus, San - - ctus Do-
San - - - ctus, San -
10
- ctus Do - mi - nus De - us, Do - mi - nus De - us Sa -
Do - mi - nus De - us, Do - mi - nus De -
Do - mi - nus De - us, Do - mi - nus De - us, Do - - mi - nus De -
- mi - nus De - us, Do - mi - nus De - us Sa - ba - oth,
- ctus Do - mi - nus De - us, San -

15
- - ba - oth, Do - - mi - nus De - us Sa - ba -
- us, Do - - mi - nus De - us Sa - ba - oth,
- us Sa - ba - oth, Do - mi - nus De - us Sa - ba -
Do - mi - nus De - us Sa - - ba - oth, Do - mi -
- - ctus Do - mi - nus De - us
20
- oth, Sa - - ba - oth. Ple - ni sunt
Do - mi - nus De - us Sa - ba - oth. Ple - ni sunt cae -
- oth, Sa - - ba - oth. Ple - - ni
- nus De - us Sa - - ba - oth. Ple - - ni sunt cae -
Sa - ba - oth. Ple - - ni
25
cae - li et ter - ra glo - - ri - a
- li et ter - ra glo - ri - a tu - a,
sunt cae - - li, ple - - ni sunt cae - li et
- li, ple - ni sunt cae - li et ter - - ra glo -
sunt cae - li et ter - ra

— tu - - a, glo - ri - a tu - a, glo - ri - a
glo - ri - a tu - a, glo - ri - a tu - a, glo - ri - a tu - a, glo - ri -
ter - ra glo - ri - a — tu - a,
- ri - a — tu - a, glo - ri - a tu -
glo - ri - a tu - a, glo - ri - a — tu -
30
tu - a, glo - ri - a tu - a, glo - ri - a — tu - a.
- a — tu - a. —
glo - ri - a — tu - a, glo - - ri - a tu - a.
- a, glo - ri - a tu - a, glo - ri - a — tu - a.
- a, glo - ri - a — tu - a.
35
Be - - ne - di - ctus, — be - - ne - di - ctus qui —
Be - ne - di - ctus — qui ve - nit, be - ne - di - ctus
Be - - ne - di - ctus, be - ne - di - ctus, be - ne - di -
Be - - ne - di - ctus,

40
ve - nit, qui ve - nit in no - mi - ne,
qui ve - nit in no - mi - ne, in
- - ctus qui ve - nit in no - mi -
be - ne - di - ctus qui ve - nit in no - mi - ne Do - mi -
45
in no - mi - ne, in no - mi - ne Do - mi - ni, in no - mi - ne Do -
no - mi - ne Do - mi - ni, in no - mi - ne, in no - - mi - ne Do -
- ne, in no - mi - ne Do - mi - ni, in no - mi - ne Do - mi - ni, in
- ni, in no - mi - ne, in no - mi - ne Do -
50
- mi - ni, in no - mi - ne, in no - mi - ne Do - mi - ni.
- mi - ni, in no - mi - ne Do - - mi - ni.
no - mi - ne Do - mi - ni, in no - mi - ne Do - mi - ni.
- mi - ni, in no - mi - ne Do - mi - ni.

𝅗𝅥 = 𝅝.
55
60
Ho - san - na in ex - cel - sis, Ho - san -
Ho - san - na in ex - cel - sis, in ex - cel - sis, Ho - san - na in ex -
Ho - san -
Ho - san - na in ex - - cel - sis, Ho - san - na in ex - cel -
Ho - san - na in ex -
65
- na in ex - cel - sis, Ho - san - na in ex - cel - sis, Ho - san -
- cel - sis, Ho - san - na in ex - cel - sis, Ho - san -
- na in ex - cel - sis in ex - - cel - sis, Ho - san -
- sis, Ho - - san - na in ex - cel - sis, in ex - cel - sis, Ho - san -
- cel - - sis, Ho - san - na in ex - cel - - sis,
70
- na in ex - cel - sis, Ho - san - na in ex - - cel - sis, [Ho - san -
- na in ex - cel - sis, Ho - san - na in ex - cel - sis, Ho - san -
- na in ex - cel - sis, Ho - san - na in ex - cel - - sis, Ho - san -
- na in ex - cel - sis, Ho - san - na in ex - cel - sis, Ho - san -
Ho - san - na in ex - cel - sis,

75
-na in ex- - cel- sis, Ho-san- -na in ex- cel- sis,
-na in ex- - cel- sis, Ho- - san-na in ex- cel- sis,
-na in ex- - cel- sis, Ho-san- - na in ex-
-na in ex- -cel- sis, Ho- san-na in ex- cel-
Ho- san- na in ex-cel- - sis,
80
in ex-cel- sis, Ho-san- na in ex- cel- sis.
Ho- san-na in ex-cel- sis, in ex- - cel- sis.
- cel- sis, Ho-san- - na in ex- cel- sis.
-sis, in ex-cel- sis, Ho-san- na in ex- cel-sis, in ex-cel- sis.
in ex-cel- sis, Ho-san- na in ex- - cel- sis.

Agnus Dei

A- gnus De- i, A-
A- - gnus De- i, A- - gnus De-
A- - gnus De-
A- - gnus De- i, A-gnus De-
A- - gnus De-

5
- gnus De - i, A - gnus De - - i,
- i, A - - gnus, A - gnus De - i, A - gnus
- i, A - gnus De - i, A - - gnus De -
- - i, A - gnus De - i, A-gnus De- -
- i, A - - gnus De - - i, A - gnus
10
qui tol - lis, qui tol- lis pec - - ca- ta mun- - di,
De - i, qui tol - lis pec - ca - ta
- i, A - gnus De - i, qui
- i, qui tol - lis pec - ca - ta mun- di, qui tol - lis
De- i, qui tol- lis pec- ca - ta mun -
15
pec- ca - ta mun - di: mi - se - re -
mun - - di: mi - - se - re - re no -
tol - lis pec - ca - ta mun - di : mi - se - re - re no - bis, mi -
pec - ca - ta mun - di : mi - se - re - re no - bis,
- di: mi - se - re - re no - bis, mi - se -

20
-re no-bis, mi- -se-re-re no- bis, mi- se- re- re no- bis,
-bis, mi- -se-re-re no- bis, mi- se- re- re no-bis,
-se-re-re no- bis, mi- se-re- re no-
mi-se-re- -re no-bis, mi-se-re-re no- bis, mi- se-re-
-re- re no- bis, mi- se- re-re no- bis,
25
mi- se-re-re no-bis, mi- -se-re-re
mi- se- re- re no- bis, mi- se- re-re no-
-bis, mi- se- re- re no- bis, mi- se- re- re no- bis,
-re no-bis, mi- se-re- re no- bis,
mi-se- -re- re no- bis, mi- se- re- re no-
30
no- bis, mi- se-re-re no-bis, mi- se-re- re no- bis.
bis, mi- -se-re- -re no- bis.
mi- se- re- re no- bis, mi- se- re-re no- bis.
-re no-bis, mi-se-re- re no- bis, mi- se-re- re no- bis.
-bis, mi-se- -re-re no- bis, mi-se- re- re no- bis.

Missa Quo puerum ediderat

Kyrie

20
25
30
- lei - son, Ky- ri- e e- lei - son, Ky-
[Ky- ri- e e- lei- - son,] Ky- ri- e e - lei- son, Ky - ri- e
Ky - - ri- e e- - lei - son, Ky- ri- e e-
- son, Ky- ri - e e - lei- son, Ky - - ri-
- lei - son, Ky- ri- e e- lei - son, Ky-
- ri- e e- lei- son, Ky- ri- e e-
e- lei- son, Ky - ri- e e- lei- son, Ky- ri- e e-
- lei- - son, Ky- - ri- e e- lei-
-e e- lei- son, Ky- - ri- e e- lei- son, Ky-
- ri- e e- lei- - son, Ky- ri- e
- lei- son. Chri - ste e -
- lei- son. Chri- ste e- lei- - son, Chri - ste e-
- son. Chri - ste e - lei - - son, Chri - ste e -
- ri- e e-lei- son. Chri- ste e- lei-
e- lei- son. Chri- ste e- lei- son, Chri -

35
- lei- son, Chri- ste e- lei- son, Chri- ste e-
- lei- son, Chri- ste e- lei- son, Chri- ste e-
- lei- son, Chri- - ste e- - lei- son, e- lei-
- son, Chri- ste e- - lei- - son, Chri- ste e-lei- son,
- ste e- - - lei- son, Chri- ste e- lei-
40
- lei- - - son, e- lei- son, Chri-
- lei- son, Chri- ste e- lei- son, [e- lei- son,] Chri- ste
- son, Chri- ste e- lei- son, Chri- ste e- lei- son, Chri- ste e-
Chri- ste e- lei- son, [e- lei- - son,] Chri-
- son, Chri- ste e- lei-
45
- ste e- lei- - son, Chri- - ste e- lei- son, Chri- ste e-lei- son, Chri-
e- lei- - son, Chri- ste e- lei- - - son,
- lei- son, e- - lei- son, Chri- ste e- lei-
- ste e- lei- son, Chri- ste e- lei- son, Chri- ste e-lei- son,
- son, Chri- ste e- lei- son, Chri- ste e- lei- son, Chri- ste e- lei- son, Chri-

50
-ste e- lei- son,Chri- ste e - lei- son,[Chri-ste e- - lei- son,] e- lei- son.
Chri- ste e- lei- son, Chri- ste e- lei- - son.
-son, Chri- - ste e- lei- son, Chri- ste e- lei- son.
Chri-ste e-lei- son,Chri- ste e-lei- son, Chri- ste e- lei- son.
-ste e- lei- son, Chri- ste e- lei- son,Chri- ste e- lei- son.
55
Ky- ri- e e- -
Ky- ri- e e- lei- son, Ky- ri- e e- lei-
Ky- ri- e e- - lei- son,Ky- ri-
Ky- ri- e e- - lei son,
Ky- ri- e e- lei- son, Ky-
60
- lei- son, Ky- - ri- e e-
-son, [e- - lei- son,]Ky- ri- e e- lei- son, Ky- ri- e
- e e- lei- - son,Ky- ri- e e- lei- son, Ky- ri- e
Ky- - ri- e e- - lei- son, Ky- - ri- e e-
-ri- e e- - lei- son,Ky- ri- e e- lei-

65
- lei- son, Ky- ri- - e e- lei- son, Ky- ri- e e- lei-
e- lei- son, [Ky- - ri- e e- lei- son,]Ky- ri- e e-
e- lei- - son,Ky- - ri- e e- lei- - son, Ky- ri-
- lei- son, Ky- ri- e e- lei- - son, Ky- ri- e
- son, Ky- - ri- e e- lei- son,
70
- son, [Ky- - ri- e e- lei- son,] Ky- ri- e e- lei-
- [lei- son, Ky- ri- e e- lei- son,] Ky- - ri- e e-
- e e- lei- son, Ky- ri- e e- lei- son, Ky- - ri- e e-
e- lei- son, Ky- ri- e e- lei- son, Ky-
Ky- ri- e e- lei- son, Ky- ri- e e- - lei- son,
75
- son, Ky- ri- e e- lei- son, [Ky- ri- e
- lei- son, Ky- - ri- e e- lei- son, Ky- ri- e e-
- lei- son, Ky- ri- e e- lei- son, [e- lei- - son,] Ky- - ri- e e-
- ri- e e- - lei- - son, Ky- ri- e e-
Ky- ri- e e- lei- son, [e- lei- son,]

80
e- lei- son, Ky- ri- e e- - lei- - son,Ky-ri- e e-
-lei- son, Ky- ri- e e- lei- - son, Ky- - ri- e e- lei- son,
- lei- - son, [Ky- ri- e e- lei- - son, Ky- ri-
-lei- son, Ky- ri- e e- lei- son, Ky- - ri- e e-
Ky- ri- e e- lei- son, Ky- ri- e e-
85
- lei- son.
Ky- ri- e e- - lei- - son.
- e e- lei- son.]
-lei- son, Ky- ri- e e- lei- son.
-lei- son, Ky- ri- e e lei- son.

Gloria

5
Et in ter- ra pax ho- mi- ni-
Et in ter- ra pax ho-mi- - ni- bus bo-
Et in ter- ra pax ho- - mi- - ni- bus bo- - nae vo-
Et in ter- ra pax ho- mi- ni- bus bo-
Et in ter- - ra pax ho- mi- - ni- bus

-bus bo- nae vo- lun-ta- tis, bo- nae vo- lun-ta- tis. Lau- da- mus
- nae vo- lun- ta- tis, bo- nae vo- lun- ta- tis. Lau-da- mus te, lau- da-
- lun- ta- - tis. Lau- da- mus te, lau-da- mus te.
- nae vo- lun- ta- tis. Lau- - da-mus te. Be- ne- di- ci- mus te. Ad-
bo- nae vo- lun- ta- tis. Lau-da-mus te. Be-
te, lau- da- - mus te. Ad- o- ra- mus te. Glo-ri- fi-
-mus te. Be- - ne- di- - ci- mus te. Glo-ri-
Be- ne- di- ci- mus te. Ad- o- ra-mus te.
-o- ra- - mus te. Glo- ri- fi- ca- mus te.
-ne- di- ci- mus te. Ad- o- ra- mus te. Glo-
-ca- mus te. Gra-
- fi- ca- mus te. Gra- ti- as a- - gi-mus ti- -
Glo- ri- fi- ca- mus te. Gra- ti- as a- gi- mus ti- -
Gra- - ti- as a- gi- mus ti-
-ri- fi- ca- mus te. Gra- ti- as a- gi- mus ti- bi

25
-ti-as a- gi- mus ti- bi pro-pter ma- gnam glo- ri- am tu-
-bi pro- pter ma- gnam glo- ri- am, pro- pter ma- gnam glo- - ri- am tu-
-bi pro- pter ma- gnam, pro- pter ma-gnam glo- ri- am tu- am. Do- mi- ne
-bi pro- pter ma- gnam, pro- pter ma- gnam, pro- pter ma- gnam glo- - ri- am tu-
pro- pter ma- gnam glo- ri- am tu- am.
30
-am. Do- - mi- ne De- us, De- us Pa- ter o-
- am. Do- mi- ne De- us, Rex cae- - le- stis, De- us Pa-
De- us, Rex cae- le- - stis, Rex cae- le- stis, De-
- am. Rex cae- le- stis, De- us Pa- ter o- mni- po- tens.
Do- mi- ne De- us, Rex cae- le- stis, Rex cae- le- stis,
35
- mni- po- tens, o- mni- po- tens, o- mni- po- tens. Do- mi-ne Fi-
-ter o- mni- po- tens. Do- mi- ne Fi- li u- - ni- ge- ni-
-us Pa- ter o- mni- po- tens. Do- mi- ne Fi- li, Do- mi- ne Fi- li
Do- mi- ne Fi- li u- ni- ge- ni- te,
De- us Pa- ter o- mni- - po- tens.

40
-li u- ni- ge- - - ni- te Je- -
-te Je- su Chri- te, Je- su Chri- ste, Je- -
u- ni- ge- ni- te Je- su Chri- ste, Je- su Chri- ste, Je- su
Do- mi- ne Fi- li u- ni- ge- - - ni- te Je- - su Chri-
Do- mi- ne Fi- li u- ni- ge- ni- te Je- su
45
-su Chri- - ste. Do- mi- ne De- us, A- - gnus De-
-su Chri- ste. Do- mi- ne De- us, A- gnus De-
Chri- ste. Do- mi- ne De- us, A- gnus De- - i,
-ste. Do- mi- ne De- us, A- gnus De- i, Do- mi- ne De- us, A-
Chri- ste, Je- su Chri- ste. Do- mi- ne De- us, A-
50
-i, Fi- - li- us Pa- tris, Fi- - li- us Pa- tris, Fi-
-i, Fi- li- us Pa- tris, Fi- li- us Pa- - tris,
Fi- li- us Pa- tris, Fi- li- us Pa- - tris, Fi- li- us Pa- tris, Fi-
-gnus De- - i, Fi- li- us Pa- tris.
-gnus De- i, Fi- li- us Pa- tris. Do- mi- ne De- us, Fi-

55
- li- us Pa- - tris. Qui tol- lis pec-
Fi- li- us Pa- tris. Qui
-li- us Pa- - tris. Qui tol- lis pec- -
- li- us Pa- tris. Qui
60
-ca- - ta mun- - di, mi- se- re-
tol- lis pec-ca- ta mun- - di, mi- se- re- re no-
-ca- ta mun- di, mi- se- re- re no- bis. Qui tol- lis
Qui tol- - lis pec- ca- - ta mun-
tol- lis pec- ca- ta mun- di, mi- - se- re-
65
- re no- bis, mi- se- re- re no- bis. Qui tol- lis pec- ca-
- bis. Qui tol- lis pec - ca-
pec- ca- ta mun- di, pec- ca- ta mun- di, qui tol - lis pec-ca- ta mun-
-di, qui tol- lis pec- - ca- ta mun- - di, pec- ca-
- re no- bis. Qui tol- lis pec- ca- ta mun- di,

70
-ta mun- di, sus- - ci- pe de- pre-
-ta mun- di, sus- ci- pe de- - pre- ca-
- di, sus- - ci- pe de- pre- ca- ti- o-
-ta mun- - di, sus- ci- pe de- pre-
sus- - ci- pe de- - pre- ca-
75
-ca- ti- o- - nem no- stram. Qui se- des ad dex- - te-ram Pa-
- ti- o- nem no- stram. mi- se-
-nem no- stram. Qui se- des ad dex- te- ram Pa-
-ca- ti- o- - nem no- stram. mi-
- ti- o- nem no- stram. Qui se- des ad dex- - te-ram Pa-
80
-tris, mi- - se- re- re no- - bis. Quo- - ni- am tu
-re- re no- bis, mi- se- re- re no- bis. Quo- ni- am
-tris, mi- se- re- re no- bis. Quo-
- se- re- re no- bis, mi- - se- re- - re no- bis.
-tris, mi- se- re- re, mi- se- re- re no- bis.

85
so- lus san- ctus. Tu so- lus Do- mi- nus. Tu so-
tu so- lus san- - ctus. Tu
-ni- am tu so- - lus san- - ctus. Tu so-
Quo- ni- am tu so- lus san- ctus. Tu so- lus Al- tis-
Tu so- lus Do- mi- nus. Tu so- lus Al-
90
-lus Al- tis- si- mus, tu so- lus Al- tis- - si- mus, Je-
so- lus Do- mi- nus. Tu so- lus Al- tis- si- mus, Je- su Chri-
-lus Al- tis- si- mus, Je- - su Chri- - ste.
-si- mus, tu so- lus Al- tis- si- mus, Je- su Chri- ste, Je- su Chri-
-tis- si- mus, tu so- lus Al- tis- si- mus, Je- - su
95
-su Chri- - ste. Cum San- cto Spi- ri-
-ste. Cum San- cto Spi- ri- tu, cum San- cto Spi- ri-
Cum San- cto Spi- ri- tu, cum San- cto Spi- ri- tu, cum San- cto
- ste. Cum San- cto Spi- ri- tu, cum San- cto Spi- ri- tu, in glo- ri- a De-
Chri- ste. Cum San- cto Spi- ri- tu, in glo- ri- a De-

100
-tu, cum San-cto Spi- - ri- tu, cum Sancto Spi- ri- tu, cum
-tu, in glo- ri- a De- i Pa- tris. Cum San-cto Spi- ri- tu, cum
Spi- ri- tu, in glo- ri- a De- i Pa- tris. A- men, Pa- tris. A- men. Cum San-
-i Pa- tris. A-men. Cum San- cto Spi- ri-
-i Pa- tris. A- men. Cum San-cto Spi- ri- tu in glo- ri- a De- i Pa- tris.
105
San- cto Spi- ri- tu, cum San- cto Spi- ri- tu, in glo- ri- a De- i
San- cto Spi- ri- tu, cum San-cto Spi- ri- tu, in glo- ri- a,
-cto Spi- ri- tu, cum San- cto Spi- ri-tu, in glo- ri- a De-
-tu, in glo- ri- a, in glo- ri- a De- i Pa-
A- men. Cum San- cto Spi- ri- tu, in glo- ri- a De- i
110
115
Pa- tris, in glo- ri- a De- i Pa- tris. A- men.
in glo- ri- a De- i Pa- tris. A- men, a- men.
-i Pa- tris, in glo- ri- a Pa- tris. [A- men,] a- men.
-tris, in glo- ri- a De- i Pa- tris. A-men, De- i Pa- tris. A- men.
Pa- tris, in glo- ri- a De- i Pa- tris. A- men.

Credo

5
Pa- - trem o- mni- po- ten- - tem,
Pa- trem o- mni- po- ten- - tem, fa- cto-
Pa- - trem o- mni- po- ten- - tem,
Pa- trem o-
Pa- - trem
10
fa- cto- rem cae- li et ter- rae, fa- - cto- rem
-rem cae- - li et ter- rae, fa-
fa- cto- rem cae- li et ter- rae, fa- cto- rem cae-
-mni- po- ten- - tem, fa- cto- rem cae- li et ter- rae,
o- mni- po- ten- tem, fa- cto- rem cae- li
cae- li et ter- - rae, et ter- rae,
-cto- rem cae- li et ter- rae, vi- - si- bi- li- um
-li et ter- rae, vi- - si- bi- li- um o-
fa- cto- rem cae- li et ter- rae, vi- si- bi-
et ter- rae, vi- si- bi- li- um o- mni- um,

15
vi- si- bi- li- um o- mni- um et in- vi- si- bi- li- um. Et in u- num
o- mni- um et in- vi- si- bi- li- um. Et in u- num
- mni- um et in-vi- si- bi- li- um. Et in u- num
-li- um o- mni- um et in-vi- - si- bi- - li- um. Et in u- num
et in- vi- si- bi- - li- um. Et in u- num Do- mi- num
20
Do- mi- num Je- sum Chri- stum,
Do- mi- num Je- - sum Chri- stum, Fi- li- um
Do- mi- num Je- sum Chri- stum, Fi- - li- um De- i u-
Do- mi- num Je- - sum Chri- stum, Fi- li- um De- i
Je- - sum Chri- stum, Fi- li- um De- i
25
Fi- li- um De- i u- - ni- ge- ni- tum. Et
De- i u- ni- ge- ni- tum. Et ex Pa- tre na- tum, et
- ni- ge- - ni- tum. Et ex Pa- tre na- tum, et
u- ni- ge- ni- tum, Fi- li- um De- i u- ni- ge- - ni- tum. Et
u- ni- ge- ni- tum, u- ni- ge- ni- tum. Et

30
ex Patre nature ante omnia
ex Pa- tre na- tum an- te o- mni-
ex Pa- tre na- tum an- te o- mni- a saecu-
ex Pa- tre na- tum an- te o- mni- a sae- cu-
ex Pa- tre na- tum an- te o- mni- a sae-
35
sae- - cu- la. De-
-a sae- - cu- la. De- um de De-
-la. De- um de De- o, lu- men de lu-
-la. De- - um de De- o, lu- men de lu- - mi- ne,
- cu- la. De- um de De- o, lu- men de lu- mi-
40
-um de De- o, lu- men de lu- mi- ne, lu- men de lu- - mi-
-o, De- - um de De- o, lu- men de lu- mi-
- mi ne, lu- men de lu- - mi- ne, De- um
lu- men de lu- mi- ne, lu- men de lu- - mi- ne,
-ne, lu- men de lu- mi- ne,

45
-ne, De- um ve- rum de De- o ve- -
-ne, De- um ve- rum de De- o ve- ro.
ve- rum de De- o ve- ro, de De- o ve-
De- um ve- - rum de De- o ve- ro. Ge-
De- um ve- rum de De- o ve-
50
-ro. Ge- ni- tum, non fa- ctum, per
Ge- ni- tum, non fa- ctum, con- sub- stan- ti- a- lem Pa- tri: per quem
-ro. con- - sub- stan- ti- a-
- ni- tum, non fa- - ctum, con- sub- stan- ti- a- lem
-ro. Ge- ni- tum, non fa- ctum,
55
quem o- mni- a, per quem o- - mni- a fa-
o- mni- a, per quem o- mni- a fa- cta sunt,
- lem Pa- tri: per quem o- mni- a, per quem o- mni- a fa- cta
Pa- tri: per quem o- mni- a fa- cta sunt. Qui
per quem o- - mni- a fa- cta

60
-cta sunt. Qui propter nos homines, et
fa- cta sunt. Qui propter nos ho- mi- nes, et pro- pter
sunt. Qui propter nos ho- mi- nes, et pro- pter no- stram sa-
pro-pter nos ho- mi- nes, et pro- pter no-stram sa- lu- tem
sunt. et pro- pter no-stram sa-
65
pro- pter no- stram sa- lu- tem de- scen- dit, de- scen-dit de cae-
no- stram sa- - lu- tem de- scen- dit de cae- lis,
-lu- tem de- scen- dit de cae- lis,
de- scen- dit, de- scen- dit de cae- lis, de- scen-dit
-lu- tem de- scen- dit de cae- lis, de- scen-
70
- lis, de- scen- - dit de cae- lis.
de- scen-dit de cae- - lis.
de- scen- - dit de cae- lis, de- scen- dit de cae- lis.
de cae- lis, de cae- - lis.
- dit de cae- lis, de cae- - lis.
75

80
Et in- - car- na- tus est de
Et in- car- na- tus est de Spi- ri-
Et in- car- na- - tus est de
Et in- car- na- tus est de Spi- ri-
Et in- car- na- tus est
85
Spi- ri- tu San- cto ex
-tu San- - cto, de Spi- - ri- tu San- cto ex Ma-
Spi- ri- tu San- cto ex Ma-
-tu San- cto, de Spi- ri- tu San- cto ex
de Spi- - ri- tu San- - cto
90
Ma- ri- a Vir- - gi- ne: Et
-ri- a Vir- - gi- ne: Et ho- - mo fa- ctus est,
-ri- a Vir- gi- ne, ex Ma- - ri- a Vir- gi- ne: Et
Ma- ri- a Vir- - gi- ne: Et ho- mo
Et ho-

95
ho- mo fa- - ctus est. Cru- ci- fi- xus e- ti- am pro no-
et ho- mo fa- ctus est. Cru- ci- fi- xus e- ti- am pro no- bis:
ho- mo fa- - ctus est. Cru-
fa- ctus est, et ho- mo fa- ctus est. Cru- ci- fi- xus e- ti-
-mo fa- ctus est. Cru- ci- fi-
100
-bis: sub Pon- ti- o Pi- la- to
sub Pon- ti- o, sub Pon- ti- o Pi- la- to pas-
-ci fi- xus e- ti- am pro no- bis: sub Pon- ti- o Pi- la-
-am pro no- bis: sub Pon- ti- o, sub Pon- ti- o Pi- la- to
-xus e- ti- am pro no- bis: sub Pon- ti- o Pi- la- to
105
pas- sus, et se- pul- tus est.
- sus, et se- pul- tus est, et se- pul- tus est.
-to pas- sus, et se- pul- - tus est.
pas- - sus, et se- pul- - tus est.
pas- - sus, et se- pul- tus est.

110
Et re- sur- re- - xit ter- - ti- a di-
Et re- sur- re- - xit, et re- sur- re-
ter- - ti- a di- -
115
- e, ter- - ti- a di- - e, se-
- xit ter- ti- a di- - e, se- cun-
-e, et re- sur- re- - xit ter- - ti- a di- - e,
120
-cun- dum Scri- ptu- ras, se- - cun-
-dum, se- cun- dum Scri- ptu- - ras.
se- cun- dum Scri- - ptu- ras.
125
-dum Scri- ptu- ras. Et a- scen- dit in cae- - lum:
Et a- scen- dit- in cae- - lum: se- det
Et a- scen- dit in cae- - lum: se-

130
se- det ad dex- te- ram Pa- - tris. Et
ad dex- te- ram Pa- tris, ad dex- te- ram Pa- tris. Et
-det ad dex- te- ram Pa- tris, ad dex- te- ram Pa- tris. Et
Et
135
i- te- rum ven- tu- - rus est cum glo- ri- a,
i- te- rum ven- tu- - rus est cum glo- ri-
i- te- rum ven- tu- rus est, ven- tu- rus est cum
i- te- rum ven- tu- rus est cum glo- ri-
140
cum glo- ri- a, ju- di- ca- re vi- vos
-a, cum glo- ri- a, ju- di- ca- re vi- - - vos et
glo- ri- a, ju- di- ca- - re vi- - vos et
-a, ju- di- ca- re vi- vos et
145
et mor- - tu- os: cu- jus re- gni non e- rit
mor- tu- os: cu- jus re- gni, cu- jus re- gni non e- rit
mor- - tu- os: cu- jus re- gni, cu- jus re- gni non
mor- tu- os: cu- jus re- gni, cu- jus re- gni non e- rit

150
fi- nis, non e- rit fi- nis, non e- rit fi-
fi- nis, non e- rit fi- nis, non e- - rit fi- nis, non
e- rit fi- - nis, non e- rit fi- nis, non e- rit
fi- nis, non e- rit fi- nis, non e- rit fi- nis, non
155
-nis, non e- rit fi- nis, non e- rit fi- nis, [fi- - nis.]
e- rit fi- nis, non e- rit fi- nis, non e- rit fi- nis.
fi- nis, non e- rit fi- nis, non e- rit fi - nis.
e- rit fi- nis, non e- rit fi- nis.
160
Et in Spi- ri- tum, et in Spi- ri- tum San- ctum
Et in Spi- ri- tum San-
Et in Spi- - ri- tum San- - ctum, Do- - mi- num,
Et in Spi- ri- tum San-
Et in Spi- ri- tum San-ctum, Do- mi- num,

165
170
Do- mi- num, et vi- vi- fi- can- tem: qui ex Pa- tre, Fi- li- o-
-ctum, Do- mi- num, et vi- vi- - fi- can- tem: qui ex Pa- - tre, Fi- li- o- que
et vi- vi- fi- can- tem: qui ex Pa- tre, Fi- li- o- que
- ctum, Do- mi- num, et vi- vi- fi- can - tem: qui ex Pa- tre, Fi - li- o-
et vi- vi- - fi- can- tem: qui ex Pa- tre, Fi- li- o- que
175
-que pro- ce- dit. Qui cum Pa- tre et Fi- li- o si- mul ad- o- ra-
pro- ce- dit. Qui cum Pa- tre et Fi- li- o si- mul ad- o- ra-
pro- ce- dit. Qui cum Pa- tre et Fi- li- o si- mul ad- o- ra-
-que pro- ce- dit. Qui cum Pa- tre et Fi- li- o si- mul ad- o-
pro- ce- dit. et Fi- li- o si- mul ad- o- ra-
180
-tur, et con- glo- ri- fi- ca- tur, et con- glo- ri- fi- ca- tur:
-tur, et con- glo- - ri- - fi- ca- tur, et con- glo-
-tur, et con- glo- ri- - fi- ca- - tur, et con- glo- ri- fi-
-ra- tur, et con- glo- ri- fi- ca- tur, et con- glo- ri- fi- ca-
- tur, et con- glo- ri-

185
qui lo- cu- - tus est per Pro- phe-
-ri- fi- ca- - tur: qui lo- cu- tus est per Pro- phe- tas.
-ca- tur: qui lo- cu- tus est per Pro- phe- tas.
- tur: Et u- nam
-fi- ca- tur: qui lo- cu- tus est per Pro- phe-
190
-tas. Et u- nam san- ctam ca- tho- li- cam et a- po-
Et u- nam sanctam ca- tho- li- cam et a- po- sto- li-
Et u- nam san- ctam ca- tho- - li- cam et a- po- sto- li-
san- ctam ca- tho- li- cam et a- po- sto- li-cam
-tas. et a- po- sto- li- cam Ec-
195
-sto- li- cam Ec- cle- si- am. Con- fi- te- or u- num ba- pti- sma in
-cam Ec- cle- - si- am. Con- fi - te- or
-cam Ec- cle- si- am. Con- fi- te- or in re- mis- si-
Ec- cle- si- am. Con- fi- te- or u- num ba- - pti-
-cle- si- am. Con- fi- te- or u- num ba- - pti-

200
re- mis- si- o- nem pec-ca- to- rum, pec- ca- - to-
in re- mis- si- o- nem pec- ca- to- - rum. Et
-o- nem pec- ca- to- rum, in re- mis- si- o- - nem
-sma in re- mis- si- o- nem pec-ca- to- rum, pec- ca- - to- rum. Et
-sma in re- mis- si- o- - nem
205
-rum. Et ex- spe- cto, et ex- spe- cto
ex- spe- - cto, et ex- spe- cto re- sur- re- cti- o-
pec- ca- to- rum. Et ex- spe- - cto, et ex- spe- cto, et ex- spe-
ex- spe- cto, et ex- spe- cto re- sur- re- cti- o-
pec- ca- to- rum. Et ex- spe- - cto re-
210
re- sur- re- cti- o- nem mor- - tu- o-
-nem, re- sur- re- cti- o- nem mor- - tu- o-
-cto re- sur- re- cti- o- nem, re- sur- re- cti- o- nem mor- - tu- o- rum.
-nem, re- sur- re- cti- o- nem, re- sur- re- cti- o- - nem mor- tu- o- -
- sur- re- cti- o- nem, re- sur- re- cti- o- nem mor- tu- o-

215
-rum. Et vi- - tam, et vi- - tam, et
- rum. Et- vi- - tam, et vi- tam, et vi-
Et vi- - tam, et vi-
- rum. Et vi- tam, et vi-
-rum. Et vi- tam, et vi-
220
vi- tam ven- tu- ri, et vi- tam ven- tu- ri sae-
- tam ven- tu- ri sae- cu- li, ven- tu- ri sae- cu-
- tam ven- tu- ri sae- - cu- li, ven- tu- ri
- tam ven- tu- ri sae- - cu- li,
-tam ven- tu- ri sae- - cu- li,
225
230
- cu- li, ven- - tu- ri sae- - - cu- li. A- men.
-li, ven- tu- ri sae- - cu- li. A- - men.
sae- cu- li. A- men, ven- tu- ri sae- cu- li. A- men.
ven- tu- ri sae- cu- li. A- men.
ven- tu- ri sae- - cu- li. A- - men.

Sanctus

San- ctus, San- - - -
San- - ctus, San- - ctus, San-
San- - - - ctus, San-
San-
San-
5
-ctus, San- - ctus Do-
- ctus, San- ctus, San- - ctus Do- mi-
- - - ctus, San- - ctus
-ctus, San- - - ctus, San-
- - - ctus, San- -
10
-mi-nus De-us Sa- ba- oth, Sa- - ba- oth. Ple-
-nus De- us Sa- ba- oth, De- us Sa- ba- oth. Ple-
Do- mi- nus De- us Sa- - ba- oth. Ple-
- - - ctus. Ple- ni- sunt
-ctus Do- mi- nus De- us Sa- ba- oth. Ple-
15

20
-ni sunt cae- li, ple- ni sunt cae- li et ter- ra
-ni sunt cae- - li, ple- ni sunt cae- - li et ter- ra
-ni sunt cae- li, ple- ni sunt cae- li et ter- - ra
cae- li, ple- ni sunt cae- li et ter- ra glo- ri-
-ni sunt cae- li et ter- ra glo-
25
glo- ri- a tu- a, glo- - ri- a tu- a,
glo- ri- a tu- a, glo- ri- a tu- a, glo- ri- a tu- a,
glo- - ri- a tu- a, glo- ri- a tu-
-a tu- a, glo- - ri- a tu- a, glo- ri- a tu- a, glo-
- ri- a tu- a, glo- ri- a tu- a,
30
glo- ri- a tu- a.
glo- ri- a tu- a, glo- ri- a tu- a.
- a, glo- ri- a tu- a, glo- ri- a tu- a.
-ri- a tu- a.
glo- ri- a tu- a, glo- ri- a tu- a.

35
Be- - ne- di- - ctus qui ve-
Be- - ne- di- - ctus qui ve- - nit, qui ve-
Be- ne- di- ctus qui ve- nit, be- - ne- - di- ctus
40
- - nit, be- ne- di- - ctus qui ve-
- - nit, be- ne- di- - ctus qui ve-
qui ve- nit, be- ne- di- ctus qui ve- nit
45
-nit in no- mi- ne Do- mi- ni,
-nit in no- mi-
in no- mi- ne Do- - mi- ni, in
50
in no- mi- ne, in no- - mi- ne Do- mi-
-ne Do- - mi- ni, in no- mi- ne Do- mi- ni, in
no- mi- ne Do- - mi- ni, in no- mi- ne, in no-

55
-ni, in no- -mi- ne Do- mi- ni.
no- mi- ne Do- - mi- ni.
-mi- ne Do- - mi- ni.
60
Ho- san- na in ex- cel- - sis,
Ho-
Ho- san- na in ex- cel- sis, ho- san-
Ho- san- na in ex- cel- sis, ho- san- na in ex- cel- sis,
Ho- san- na in ex- cel- sis, ho-
65
ho- san- na in ex- cel- sis, ho- san- na
- san- na in ex- - cel- sis, ho- san- na in
-na in ex- cel- - sis, ho- san- na in ex- cel- sis,
ho- san- na in ex- cel- sis, ho- san- na in ex- cel-
-san- na in ex- cel- sis,

70
in ex- - cel- sis, ho- san- na in ex-
ex- cel- - sis, ho- san- na in ex- cel- - sis, ho-
in ex- cel- - sis, ho- san- na in ex- cel-
-sis, in ex- - cel- sis, in ex- - cel-
ho- san- na in ex- cel- - sis,
75
- cel- sis, in ex- - cel- sis.
-san- na in ex- cel- sis, in ex- cel- sis.
-sis, in ex- cel- sis, in ex- cel- sis.
-sis, ho- san- na in ex- cel- - sis.
in ex- cel- sis, in ex- cel- sis.

Agnus Dei

5
A- gnus De- i, A- gnus De- - i, A- gnus
A- gnus De- i, A- gnus De-
A- - gnus De- i, A- gnus De- i, A- -

10
De- i, A- gnus De- i, A- gnus De-
- i, A- - gnus De- - i, A- gnus De- i,
A- gnus De- i, A- gnus De- i, A-
-gnus De- i, A- - - gnus De- i, A-
A- - gnus De- i, A- gnus De- i,
15
-i, [A- gnus De- i,] qui tol- lis pec- ca- ta
A- gnus De- i, A- gnus De- i, qui tol- lis pec- ca-
- gnus De- i, qui tol- lis pec- ca- ta mun- di, pec- ca- ta
- gnus De- i, qui tol- lis pec- ca- ta mun- di,
A- gnus De- i, A- gnus De- i,
20
mun- - di, qui tol- - lis pec-
-ta mun- - di, pec- - ca- ta mun- di:
mun- di, qui tol- lis pec- ca- ta mun- di:
qui tol- lis pec- ca- ta mun- di, qui tol- lis
qui tol- lis pec- ca- ta mun- di, qui tol-

25
- ca- ta mun- di: mi- se- re- re no- bis,
mi- se- re- - re no- bis, mi- se- re- - re no- - bis,
mi- se- re- re no- - bis, mi-
pec- ca- ta mun- di: mi- se- re- re no- - bis,
-lis pec- ca- ta mun- di: mi-
30
mi- se- re- re no- bis, mi- se- re- re, mi-
mi- - se-re- re no- bis, mi- se- re- re no- bis, mi-
- se- re- re no- - bis, mi-se- re- re no- bis, mi- se- re- re no- bis, mi- se-
mi- se- re- re no- bis, mi- se- re- re no- bis,
-se- re- re no- bis, mi- se- re- re no- bis, mi-
35
-se- re- re, mi- se- - re- re no- bis.
-se- re- re no- bis.
-re- re no- bis.
mi- se- re- re, mi- se- re- re no- bis.
-se- re- re no- bis, mi- se- re- re no- bis.

Missa Amor ecco colei

Kyrie

15
-son, [e- lei- son,]Chri- ste e- lei- son, Chri- ste e-
e- lei- - son, Chri- ste e- lei- son,
-son, Chri- ste e- lei- son, Chri- - ste e- lei- son, Chri- ste e-
20
-lei- son, Chri- ste e- lei- son, Chri-
Chri- ste e- lei- son, [Chri- ste e- lei- son,] Chri- ste e- lei- son, Chri-
-lei- son, Chri- ste e- lei- son,
25
- ste e- lei- son, Chri- - ste e- lei- son.
-ste e- lei- son, Chri- ste e- lei- - son.
Chri- ste e- lei- son.
30
Ky- ri- e e- lei- son, Ky- ri- e,
Ky- ri- e e- lei- son,Ky- ri- e e- lei- son,
Ky- ri- e e- lei- son, Ky- ri- e e- lei-
Ky- ri- e e- lei- son, Ky- ri- e e- lei- son, Ky- ri-
Ky- ri- e e- lei- son, Ky-

Ky- ri- e e- lei- son, [Ky- ri- e]
Ky- ri- e e- lei- -
-son, Ky- ri- e e- lei- son, Ky- ri- e e- lei- son, Ky-
-e e- lei- son, Ky- - ri- e e-
-ri- e e- lei- son,
35
e- lei- son, Ky- ri- e e- lei- son.
-son, Ky- ri- e e- lei- son.
-ri- e e- lei- son, Ky- ri- e e- lei- son.
-lei- son, Ky- - ri- e e- lei- son.
Ky- ri- e e- lei- son, Ky- ri- e e- lei- son.

Gloria

ho- mi- - ni- bus bo- nae vo- lun- ta-
Et in ter- ra pax ho- mi- ni- bus bo- nae vo- lun- ta-
Et in ter- ra pax ho- mi- ni- bus bo- nae vo- lun- ta- tis.
Et in ter- ra pax ho- mi- - ni- bus, ho- mi- ni- bus bo- nae vo-
Et in ter- ra pax ho- mi- ni- bus, ho- mi- ni- bus bo- nae

5
- -tis. Lau- da- mus te. Be- ne- di- ci- mus te.
-tis. Lau- da- mus te. Be- ne- di- ci- mus te.
Lau- da- mus te, lau- da- mus te. Be- ne- di- ci- mus te.
-lun- ta- tis. Lau-da- mus te. Be- ne- di- ci- mus te.
vo- lun- ta- tis. Lau- da- mus te.
10
Ad- o- ra- - mus te. Glo- ri- fi- ca- mus te.
Ad- o- ra- - mus te. Glo- ri- fi- ca- mus te, glo- ri- fi- ca- mus te.
Ad- o- ra- mus te. Glo- ri- fi- ca- mus te, glo- ri- fi- ca- mus te. Gra-
Ad- o- ra- - mus te. Glo- ri- fi- ca- mus te, glo- ri- fi- ca- mus
Ad- o- ra- mus te. Glo- ri- fi- ca- mus te, glo- ri- fi- ca- mus te.
15
Gra- ti- as a- gi- mus ti- bi pro- pter ma- gnam glo- ri- am tu- am. Do- mi- ne
Gra- ti- as a- gi- mus ti- bi pro- pter ma- gnam glo- ri- am tu- am. Do- mi- ne
- ti- as a- gi- mus ti- bi pro- pter ma- gnam glo- ri- am tu- am.
-te. pro- pter ma- gnam glo- ri- am tu- am. Do- mi- ne
Gra- ti- as a- gi- mus ti- bi Do- mi- ne

De - us, Rex cae - le - stis, De - us Pa - ter o - mni - po - tens.
De - us, Rex cae - le - stis, De - us Pa - ter o - mni - po - tens. Do-
De - us Pa - ter o - mni - po - tens. Do-
De - us, Rex cae - le - stis, De - us Pa - ter o - mni - po - tens. Do-
De - us, Rex cae - le - stis, De - us Pa - ter o - mni - po - tens.
20
Do - mi - ne Fi - li u - ni - ge - ni - te Je - su Chri - ste.
-mi - ne Fi - li u - ni - ge - ni - te Je - su Chri - ste, Je - su Chri-
-mi - ne Fi - li u - ni - ge - ni - te Je - su Chri - ste.
-mi - ne Fi - li u - ni - ge - ni - te Je - su Chri - ste.
u - ni - ge - ni - te Je - su Chri-
25
Do - mi - ne De - us, A - gnus De - i, Fi - li - us Pa-
-ste. Do - mi - ne De - us, A - gnus De - i, Fi - li - us Pa - tris, Fi-
Do - mi - ne De - us, Do - mi - ne De - us, A - gnus De - i, Fi-
Do - mi - ne De - us, A - gnus De - i, Fi - li - us Pa - tris, Fi-
-ste. Do - mi - ne De - us, A - gnus De - i, Fi - li - us Pa - tris, Fi-

30
- tris. Qui tol- lis pec- ca- ta mun- di, mi- se- re- re no-
-li- us Pa- tris. Qui tol- lis pec- ca- ta mun- di, mi- se- re- re no-
-li- us Pa- tris. Qui tol- lis pec- ca- ta mun- di, mi- se- re- re no-
- li- us Pa- tris. Qui tol- lis pec- ca- ta mun- di, mi- se- re- re no-
- li- us Pa- tris. mi- se- re- re no-
35
-bis. Qui tol- lis pec- ca- ta mun- di, sus- ci- pe de- pre- ca- ti- o- nem no-
-bis. Qui tol- lis pec- ca- ta mun- di, sus- ci- pe de- pre- ca-
-bis. Qui tol- lis pec- ca- ta mun- di, sus- ci- pe de- pre- ca- ti- o- nem no-
-bis. Qui tol- lis pec- ca- ta mun- di, sus- ci- pe de- pre- ca-
-bis. Qui tol- lis pec- ca- ta mun- di sus- ci- pe de- pre- ca- ti- o- nem no-
40
-stram, de- pre- ca- ti- o- - nem no- stram. Qui se- des ad dex- te- ram Pa-
-ti- o- nem no- stram. Qui se- des
-stram, de- pre- ca- ti- o- - nem no- stram. Qui se- des ad dex- te- ram Pa-
- ti- o- nem no- stram. Qui se- des ad dex- te- ram Pa-
-stram. Qui se- des ad dex- te- ram Pa- tris,

- tris, Quo- ni- am tu so- lus san- ctus.
mi- se- re- re no- bis. Quo- ni- am tu so- lus san-ctus. Tu
-tris, mi- se- re- re no- bis. Quo- ni- am tu so- lus san- ctus. Tu
-tris, mi- se- re- re no- bis. Quo- ni- am tu so- lus san- ctus. Tu
mi- se- re- re no- bis. Tu
45
Tu so- lus Al- tis- si- mus, Je- su Chri- ste. Cum
so- lus Do- mi- nus. Tu so- lus Al- tis- si- mus, Je- - su Chri- ste. Cum
so- lus Do- mi- nus. Tu so- lus Al- tis- si- mus, Je- su Chri- ste. Cum
so- lus Do- mi- nus. Tu so- lus Al- tis- si- mus, Je- su Chri- ste. Cum
so- lus Do- mi- nus. Tu so- lus Al- tis- si- mus, Je- su Chri- ste.
50
San- cto Spi- ri- tu, cum San- cto Spi- ri- tu, in glo- ri- a De- i Pa- tris. A-
San- cto Spi- ri- tu, cum San- cto Spi- ri- tu, in glo- ri- a De- i Pa- tris. A- men, in
San- cto Spi- ri- tu, cum San- cto Spi- ri- tu, in glo- ri- a De- i
San- cto Spi- ri- tu, cum San- cto Spi- ri- tu, in glo- ri- a De- i,
Cum San- cto Spi- ri- tu, in glo- ri- a De- i Pa-

55
-men, in glo-ri- a De-i Pa- tris. A- men.
glo-ri-a De-i, in glo-ri-a De-i Pa- -tris. A- men.
Pa- tris. A-men, in glo-ri-a De-i Pa- tris. A- men.
in glo-ri-a De-i Pa- tris. A- men, a- men.
-tris, in glo- ri-a De- i Pa- tris. A- men.

Credo

fa- cto- rem cae- li et
Pa- trem o-mni- -po-ten-tem, fa-cto- rem cae-
Pa-trem o-mni- -po-ten- tem, fa- cto- rem cae- li
Pa-trem o- mni-po- ten- tem, fa- cto- rem cae- li
Pa- trem o-mni- -po-ten-tem, fa-
5
ter- rae, fa-cto-rem cae- li et ter-rae, vi-si- bi-li-um, vi-si-bi-li-
-li et ter- rae, vi- si-bi-li- um o- mni-
et ter- rae, et ter- - rae, vi- -si-bi-li-um o-
et ter- rae, et ter- rae, vi- si-bi-li-um
-cto- rem cae- li et ter- rae, vi- si-

10
-um o - mni - um et in - vi - si - bi - li - um.
-um et in - vi - si - bi - li - um. Et in u - num
- mni - um et in - vi - si - bi - li - um.
o - mni - um et in - vi - si - bi - li - um. Et in u - num
-bi - li - um o - mni - um Et in u - num
Et in u - num Do - mi - num Je - sum Chri - stum, Fi - li -
Do - mi - num Je - sum Chri - stum,
Je - sum Chri - stum, Fi - li - um De - i,
Do - mi - num Je - sum Chri - stum, Fi - li - um
Do - mi - num Je - sum Chri - stum, Fi -
15
-um De - i, Fi - li - um De - i u - ni - ge - ni - tum.
Fi - li - um De - i u - ni - ge - ni - tum. Et ex
Fi - li - um De - i u - ni - ge - ni - tum, u - ni - ge - ni - tum.
De - i u - ni - ge - ni - tum, u - ni - ge - ni -
- li - um De - i u - ni - ge - ni - tum, u - ni - ge - ni - tum.

20
Et ex Pa-tre na - tum De - um de
Pa - tre na - tum an - - te o-mni-a sae- - cu-la. De-um de
Et ex Pa-tre na-tum an-te o-mni- a sae - cu - la. De-um
tum. Et ex Pa-tre na-tum an - te o - mni-a sae - cu - la. De - um
an - - te o-mni-a sae - cu - la.
25
De-o, lu - men de lu-mi-ne, De - um ve-rum de De-o ve-ro. Ge-
De - o, lu - men de lu-mi-ne, De-um ve-rum de De- o ve - ro.
de De-o, lu-men de lu-mi-ne, De - um ve-rum de De-o ve - ro.
de De-o, De-um ve-rum de De - o ve-ro.
lu - men de lu-mi-ne, De - um ve-rum de De-o ve-
ni-tum, non fa - ctum, con- sub-stan - ti - a-lem Pa - tri: per quem o-mni-
Ge - ni-tum, non fa - ctum, con-sub-stan-ti - a- lem Pa-tri: per
Ge - ni-tum, non fa - ctum, con-sub-stan-ti - a - lem Pa-tri: per quem o-mni-
per quem o - mni - a
ro. per quem o-mni-

30
-a, per quem o - mni - a fa - cta sunt. Qui
___ quem o - mni - a fa - cta sunt.
-a, per quem o - mni - a, per quem o - mni - a fa - cta sunt. Qui___
fa - cta sunt, fa - cta sunt, per quem o - mni - a fa - cta sunt.
-a, fa - cta sunt, per quem o - mni - a fa - cta sunt. Qui___
35
pro - pter nos ho - mi - nes, et pro - pter no - stram sa - lu - tem de -
et pro - pter no - stram sa - lu - tem de - scen - dit de cae -
___ pro - pter nos ho - mi - nes, et pro - pter no - stram sa - lu - tem de - scen - dit de cae -
Qui pro - pter nos ho - mi - nes, et pro - pter no - stram sa - lu - tem de - scen - dit de cae -
___ pro - pter nos ho - mi - nes, de - scen - dit de cae -
40
- scen - dit de cae - lis, de - scen - dit de cae - lis. Et in - car -
-lis, de - scen - dit de cae - lis, de - scen - dit de cae - lis. Et in -
- lis, de - scen - dit de cae - lis. Et in -
- lis, de - scen - dit de cae - lis, de - scen - dit de cae - lis. Et in -
- lis, de - scen - dit de cae - lis, de - scen - dit de cae - lis. Et

45
-na - tus est de Spi - ri - tu San - cto ex Ma - ri - a
- car-na-tus est ex Ma-ri-a Vir-gi-
- car-na - tus est de Spi-ri-tu San- cto ex Ma- ri - a Vir - gi - ne :
- car-na-tus est de Spi-ri - tu San - cto ex Ma - ri- a Vir - - gi-ne:
in-car-na-tus est de Spi-ri-tu San - cto ex Ma - ri - a Vir-
50
Vir-gi-ne: Et ho - mo fa - ctus, fa - ctus est.
-ne: Et ho-mo fa - ctus, fa - ctus est. e - ti -
Et ho- mo fa - ctus est, et ho-mo fa - ctus est. Cru- - ci-fi-xus
Et ho - mo fa - ctus est. Cru- - ci-fi-xus e-
- gi - ne: Et ho - mo fa - ctus est. Cru - - ci-fi-xus
55
e - ti-am pro no - bis: sub Pon-ti- o Pi - la - to pas-
- am pro no-bis: sub Pon-ti - o Pi-la - to, Pi - la - to pas - sus,
e - ti - am pro no-bis: sub Pon- ti- o Pi - la - to
- ti-am pro no - bis: sub Pon - ti - o Pi - la - to pas-
e - ti-am pro no-bis: sub Pon - ti- o Pi-la - to pas-

60
- sus, et se - pul - tus est.
et se - pul - - tus est.
pas - - sus, et se - pul - tus est.
- sus, et se - - pul - tus est.
- sus, et se - pul - tus est.
65
Et re - sur - re - xit ter - ti - a di - e, ter - ti - a di - e,
ter - ti - a di - e, et re - sur - re - xit ter -
Et re - sur - re - xit ter - ti - a di - e, ter -
ter - ti - a di - e, ter - ti - a di - e.
70
ter - ti - a di - e, se - cun - dum Scri - ptu - ras, se - cun - dum Scri -
- ti - a di - e, se - cun - dum Scri - ptu - ras, se - cun - dum Scri - ptu -
- ti - a di - e, se - cun - dum Scri - ptu - ras, se - cun - dum Scri - ptu -
Et re - sur - re - xit ter - ti - a di - e, se - cun - dum Scri - ptu -
- ptu - ras. Et a - scen - dit in cae - lum: se - det ad dex - te - ram Pa - tris, se -
- ras. Et a - scen - dit in cae - lum: se - det ad dex - te - ram, se -
- ras. Et a - scen - dit in cae - lum: se - det ad dex - te - ram Pa -
- ras. Et a - scen - dit in cae - lum: se - det ad

75
- det ad dex - te - ram Pa - - tris. ven - tu - rus est
- det ad dex - te - ram Pa - tris. Et i - te - rum cum glo - ri -
-tris, se - det ad dex - - te - ram Pa - tris. Et i - te - rum cum glo - ri -
dex - te - ram Pa - tris. ven - tu - rus est
80
ju - di - ca - re vi - vos et mor - tu - os: cu - jus re -
- a, vi - vos et mor - - tu - os: cu - jus
- a, ju - di - ca - re vi - vos et mor - - tu - os: cu - jus
ju - di - ca - re vi - vos et mor - - tu - os:
85
- gni non e - rit fi - nis, non e - - rit fi - nis.
re - gni non e - rit fi - nis, non e - rit fi - nis.
re - gni non e - rit fi - nis, non e - rit fi - nis.
cu - jus re - gni non e - rit fi - nis.
90
Et in Spi - ri - tum San - ctum, Do - mi - num, et vi - vi - fi - can -
Et in Spi - ri - tum San - ctum, Do - mi - num, et vi - vi - fi - can -
Et in Spi - ri - tum San - ctum, Do - mi - num, et vi - vi - fi - can - tem: qui
Et in Spi - ri - tum San - ctum, Do - mi - num, et vi - vi - fi - can -
Et in Spi - ri - tum et vi - vi - fi - can -

- tem: qui ex Pa - tre, Fi - li - o - que pro - ce -
- tem: qui ex Pa - tre, Fi - li - o - que pro - ce - dit, Fi - li - o - que pro - ce -
___ ex Pa - tre, Fi - li - o - que pro - ce - - dit, Fi - li - o - que pro - ce -
- tem: qui ex Pa - tre Fi - li - o - que pro - - ce - dit.
- tem: qui ex Pa - tre, Fi - li - o - que pro - ce - dit.
95
- dit. Qui cum Pa - tre ___ et Fi - li - o si - - mul ad - o - ra - tur,
- dit. Qui cum Pa - tre ___ et Fi - li - o si - - mul ad - o - ra - tur, et
- dit. Qui cum Pa - tre et Fi - li - o si - - mul ad - o - ra - tur,
Qui cum Pa - tre si - - mul ad - o -
et Fi - li - o si - - mul ad - o - ra - tur, et
100
et con - glo - - ri - fi - ca - tur, et con - glo -
con - glo - ri - fi - ca - tur, et con - glo - ri - fi - ca -
et con - glo - ri - fi - ca - tur, et con - glo - ri - fi - ca - tur, et con - glo -
- ra - tur, et con - glo - ri - fi - ca - tur:
con - glo - ri - fi - ca - tur:

-ri - fi - ca - tur : qui lo - cu - tus est per Pro - phe -
- tur : qui lo - cu - tus est per
-ri - fi - ca - tur : qui lo - cu - tus est, qui lo - cu - tus
qui lo - cu - tus est per Pro - phe - tas, per Pro - phe -
qui lo - cu - tus est per
105
- tas. ca - tho - li - cam, ca - tho - li - cam, ca -
Pro - phe - tas. ca - tho - li - cam, ca -
est per Pro - phe - tas. Et u - nam san - ctam ca - tho - li -
- tas, per Pro - phe - tas. Et u - nam san - ctam ca - tho - li - cam, ca -
Pro - phe - tas. Et u - nam san - ctam ca - tho - li - cam,
- tho - li - cam et a - po - sto - li - cam, et a - po -
- tho - li - cam, ca - tho - li - cam et a - po - sto - li - cam, et
- cam, ca - tho - li - cam et a - po - sto - li - cam Ec - cle - si - am,
- tho - li - cam, ca - tho - li - cam et a - po - sto - li - cam, et a - po - sto - li -
ca - tho - li - cam et a - po - sto - li - cam Ec - cle - si - am, et

110
- sto - li - cam Ec - cle - si - am. Con - fi - te - or u -
a - po - sto - li - cam Ec - - cle - si - am. Con - fi - te - or
et a - po - sto - li - cam Ec - cle - si - am. Con - fi - te - or
- cam Ec - cle - si - am. Con - - fi - te - or u -
a - po - sto - li - cam Ec - cle - si - am. Con - fi - te - or u -
115
- nam ba - pti - sma in re-mis-si - o - nem pec-ca - to - rum. Et ex -
in re-mis-si - o - nem pec-ca - to - rum. Et
u - nam ba - pti - sma in re-mis-si - o - nem pec-ca - to - rum.
- nam ba - pti - sma in re-mis-si - o - nem pec-ca - to - rum. Et ex - spe -
- nam ba - pti - sma in re-mis-si - o - nem pec-ca - to - rum. Et ex -
120
- spe - cto, et ex - spe - cto re - sur - re - cti - o - nem mor - tu - o - rum.
ex - spe - cto, et ex - spe - cto re - sur - re - cti - o - nem mor - tu - o - rum. Et
Et ex - spe - cto re - sur - re - cti - o - nem mor - tu - o -
- cto re - sur - re - cti - o - nem mor - tu - o -
- spe - cto re - sur - re - cti - o - nem mor - tu - o - rum.

125
Et vi - tam ven - tu - ri, ven - tu - ri sae - cu - li. A - men,
vi - tam ven - tu - ri sae - - cu - li. A - men, ven - tu - ri
- rum. Et vi - tam ven - tu - ri sae - cu - li. A - men,
- rum. Et vi - tam ven - tu - ri sae - cu - li. A - men, ven - tu - ri sae - cu -
Et vi - tam ven -
ven - tu - ri sae - cu - li, ven - tu - ri sae - cu - li. A -
sae - cu - li, ven - tu - ri sae - cu - li, ven - tu - ri sae - cu - li. A -
ven - tu - ri sae - cu - li. A - men, ven - tu - ri sae - cu -
- li, ven - tu - ri sae - cu - li. A - men, sae - cu -
- tu - ri sae - cu - li, ven - tu - ri sae - cu - li. A -
130
- men.
- men, ven - tu - ri sae - cu - li. A - - men.
- li. A - men, ven - tu - ri sae - cu - li. A - men.
- li. A - men.
- men, a - - men.

Sanctus

San - ctus, San -
San - ctus, San - ctus, San - ctus
San - ctus, San - ctus
San - ctus, San -
San - ctus, San -
5
ctus Do - mi-nus De - us Sa - ba - oth, Do - mi - nus De - us Sa -
Do - mi - nus De - us, Do - mi - nus De - us
Do - mi - nus De - us Sa - ba - oth, Do - mi - nus De -
ctus Do - mi nus De - us Sa - ba - oth, Do -
ctus, [San - ctus] Do - mi - nus De - us Sa - ba - oth,
10
ba - oth, Do - mi - nus De - us Sa - ba -
Sa - ba - oth, Do - mi - nus De - us Sa - ba - oth, De -
us Sa - ba - oth, Do - mi - nus De - us Sa -
mi - nus De - us Sa - ba - oth, Do - mi - nus De -
Do - mi - nus De - us Sa -

15
-oth. Ple - ni sunt cae - li, ple -
-us Sa - ba - oth. Ple - ni sunt cae -
- ba - oth. Ple - ni sunt cae - li et ter - ra,
-us Sa - ba - oth. Ple - ni sunt cae - - li et
-ba - oth. Ple - ni sunt cae - li et
20
-ni sunt cae - li et ter - - ra glo - ri - a tu - a.
- li et ter - ra glo - ri - a tu - a.
et ter - ra glo - ri - a tu - a.
ter - ra, et ter - ra glo - ri - a tu - a.
ter - ra glo - ri - a tu - a.
25
Be - - ne - di - ctus qui ve -
Be - ne - - di - - ctus, be - ne - - di - ctus qui
Be - ne - di - ctus qui ve - -
30
- nit, be - - ne - di - - ctus qui ve -
ve - nit, qui ve - nit, be - - ne - di - ctus qui ve -
- nit, be - ne - di - ctus qui ve - -

35
-nit in no- - mi- ne Do-
-nit in no- - mi- ne Do- mi- ni,
-nit in no- mi- ne Do- -
40
- mi- ni, in no- mi- ne Do- mi- ni.
in no- - mi- ne Do- - mi- ni.
- mi- ni, in no- - mi- ne Do- mi- ni.
45
Ho- san- na in ex- cel- - sis, Ho- san-
Ho- san- na in ex- cel- sis, in ex- cel- sis,
Ho- san- - na in ex- cel- sis, Ho- san-
Ho- san- - na in
Ho- san- - na
50
-na in ex- cel- sis, Ho- - san- na in ex- cel-
Ho- san- - na in ex- cel- sis, Ho- san- na
-na in ex- cel- sis, in ex- cel- sis, Ho- san- na in ex-cel-
ex- cel- - sis, Ho- san- na in ex- cel-
in ex- cel- - sis, Ho- san- na in ex- cel- sis, Ho-

55
-sis, in ex- - cel- sis, in ex- cel- sis.
in ex-cel- sis, Ho- san- na in ex- - cel- sis.
-sis, Ho- san- na in ex- cel- - sis, in ex- cel- sis.
-sis, Ho- san- na in ex- cel- sis.
-san- na in ex- - cel- - sis.

Agnus Dei

A- gnus De- i, A- - gnus De- - i, [A- gnus De- i,] qui tol- lis
A - gnus De- - i, A- gnus De- - i, A- gnus De- i, A- gnus De- i, [A-
A- gnus De- i, A- - - gnus De- i, A- gnus De- i,
A- gnus De- i, A- - gnus De- i, qui tol- lis
5
A- gnus De- i, A- - gnus

10
De - i, qui tol - lis pec - ca - ta mun - di, qui
pec - ca - ta, qui tol - lis pec - ca - ta mun - di: mi - se - re -
- gnus De - i,] qui tol - lis pec - ca - ta mun - di: mi -
qui tol - lis pec - ca - ta mun - di, pec - ca - ta mun - di:
pec - ca - ta mun - di, qui tol - lis pec - ca - ta
15
tol - lis pec - ca - ta mun - di: mi - se - re - re no - bis, mi - se - re - re
- re no - bis, mi - se - re - re no - bis, mi - se - re - re
- se - re - re no - bis, mi - se - re - re no - bis, mi - se - re - re
mi - se - re - re no - bis, mi - se - re - re no - bis, mi - se - re - re no -
mun - di: mi - se - re - re - no - bis, mi - se - re - re no - bis,
20
no - bis, mi - se - re - re no - bis, mi - se - re - re no - bis.
no - bis, mi - se - re - re no - bis, mi - se - re - re no - bis.
no - bis, mi - se - re - re no - bis.
- bis, mi - se - re - re no - bis, mi - se - re - re no - bis.
mi - se - re - re no - bis, mi - se - re - re no - bis.

Antiphon Vidi aquam

15
a la- - te - re dex - -
la - te - re dex - tro, a la - te - re dex - tro, a la -
- plo, a la - te - re dex - tro, a la - te - re dex - tro, a la - te -
- te - re dex- - tro, a la- - te - re
20
- tro, al- - le - - lu - -
- te - re dex - tro, al - le - - lu - ia, al - le - lu - ia, al - le - lu - ia, al -
- re dex- tro, al - - le - lu - ia, al - le - lu - ia, al - - le lu - ia,
dex - tro, al - le - lu - ia, al - le - lu - ia, al - le - lu -
25
- - ia. Et o -
- le - lu - - ia, al - le - lu - ia, al - - le - lu - ia. Et
al - le - - lu - ia, al - le - - lu - ia. Et
- ia, al - le - lu - ia. Et
30
- mnes, ad quos per - ve - nit a - qua i-
o - mnes, ad quos per - ve - nit a - -
o - - mnes, ad quos per - ve - nit a - - qua
o - mnes, ad quos per - ve - nit a - qua i - sta, a -

35
-sta, a - qua i - sta, sal - - vi fa - cti
- qua, a - - qua i - sta sal - - vi fa -
i - sta, sal - - - vi
- qua i - sta,
sal -
40
sunt, sal - - vi fa - cti
- cti sunt, sal - vi fa - cti sunt,
fa - cti sunt,
- - vi fa - cti sunt,
45
sunt, et di - - cent, et di -
et di - - cent, al - - le - lu - ia, a - le - lu -
et di - cent,
et di - - cent, al -
- cent, al - le - - lu - ia, al - le - lu -
- ia, al - le - lu - ia, al - le - lu - ia, al - le - - lu -
al - le - lu - ia,
- le - lu - ia, al -

* In the source, this ligature is in the shape of a podatus, with the upper note colored.

** In the source, the tied note is notated as a half-coloration.

Glo-ri-a Pa-tri, et Fi-li-o, et Spi-ri- tu- i San- cto.
Si- cut e- rat in prin- ci-pi-o, in prin- ci- pi-o, et nunc, et sem- per, et in sae- cu-la sae- cu-lo- rum. A- men.
Si-cut e- rat in prin- ci- pi- o, in prin- ci- pi- o, et nunc, et sem- per, et in sae-cu- la sae- cu- lo- rum. A- men, a- men.
Si- cut e- rat in prin- ci- pi- o, et nunc, et sem- per, et in sae-cu- la sae- cu- lo- rum. A- men, sae- cu- lo- rum. A- men.
Si- cut e- rat in prin- ci- pi- o, et nunc et sem- per, et in sae- cu- la sae- cu- lo- rum. A- men, sae- cu- lo- rum. A- men.
70
75

Magnificat Vivre ne puis sur terre

10
in De- o, in De - o sa -
me - us: in De - o, [in De - o] sa -
vit spi - ri - tus me- us: in De - o, in De - o sa - lu -
ri - tus me - us: in De - o sa - lu - ta - ri
in De - o, in De - o sa -
ri - tus me - us: in De - o, in De - o,
15
lu - ta - ri me - o, in De - o sa - lu - ta - ri me -
lu - ta - ri me - o, in De - o sa - lu -
ta - ri me - o, sa - lu - ta - ri me - o, sa - lu - ta - ri me -
me - o, sa - lu - ta - ri me - o, sa - lu -
lu - ta - ri me - o, sa - lu - ta - ri me - o, [sa - lu - ta - ri me - o,]
in De - o sa - lu - ta - ri

20
- o. Qui - a fe -
- ta- ri me - o, sa- - lu- ta - ri me - o.
-o, sa- lu- ta - ri me - o. Qui - a fe -
- ta- ri me - o. Qui - a fe -
sa - lu - ta - ri me - o. Qui - a fe -
me - o, sa - lu - ta - ri me - o.

25
- cit mi - hi ma - - gna qui po - - tens est, qui
Qui - a fe - cit mi - hi ma - -
- cit mi - hi ma - - gna qui po - tens est, qui-
- cit mi - hi ma - gna, qui - a fe - cit mi - hi
- cit mi - hi ma - - gna qui po - tens est,
Qui - a fe - cit mi - hi ma -

30
po-tens est, qui po - tens est:
- gna qui po - tens est, qui po - tens est, qui po - - tens est, qui
- a fe - cit mi - - hi ma - gna qui po - tens
ma - gna qui po - tens est, qui po - tens
mi - hi ma - gna qui po - - tens est, po - - tens
- gna qui po - - tens est, qui po-tens est, [qui po - tens

35
et san - ctum no-men e - - jus, et san - ctum no - men
po - tens est: et san - ctum no - men e - jus, et san -
est: et san - ctum no - men e - jus, et san - ctum no - men e - jus,
est: et san - ctum no - men e - jus, et san -
est: et san - ctum no-men e - jus, et san - ctum no - men e - jus, et
est:] et sanctum no-men e - - jus, et

40
e - jus, et san - ctum no - men e - jus, et san - ctum
- ctum, et san - ctum no - men e - jus.
et san - ctum no - men e - jus, et san - ctum
- ctum no - men e - jus, et san - ctum no - men e - jus.
san - ctum no - men e - jus, et san - ctum no - men e - jus, et san -
san - ctum no - men e - jus, et san - ctum no - men e - jus, et san - ctum
45
no - men e - jus. Fe - cit po - ten -
Fe - cit po - ten - ti - am, fe -
no - men e - jus. Fe - cit po - ten - ti - am, fe -
Fe - cit po - ten - ti - am,
- ctum no - men e - jus. Fe -
no - men e - jus.

50
- - ti- am in bra- - chi- o su- o:
- cit po - ten- - - ti - am in bra- chi- o su- o:
- cit po- ten- - ti- am in bra- chi-
fe- cit po - ten- - ti am in bra- - chi - o
- cit po - ten- - ti - am in bra- chi- o su - o, in bra-
in bra- chi- o su - o, in bra- chi-
55
di - sper- - sit su - per-
di - sper - - sit, di- sper - sit su - per-
- o su - o, [in bra- chi- o su - o:] di- sper - - sit su - per -
su - o: di- sper - sit su - per - bos
- chi - o su- - o: su - per - bos
- o su - o: di- sper- sit su - per- bos

60
- bos mente cordis su - i, mente
- bos men - te cor - - dis su - - i, men - te cor - dis su - i,
- bos men - te, men - te cor - dis
men - te cor - - dis su - i, men - te, men - te cor - dis su -
men - te cor - dis su - i, men - te, men -
men - te cor - dis su - i, men - te, men - te cor -
65
cor - dis su - - i.
men - te cor - dis su - - i.
su - i, men - te cor - dis su - i.
- i, men - te cor - dis su - i.
- te cor - dis su - - i.
- dis su - i, men - te cor - dis su - i.
70

75
E - su - ri - en - - tes im - ple - vit
E - su - ri - en - - tes im - ple - - vit
E - su - ri en - - tes, e - su - ri - en - -
E - su - ri - en - - tes im - ple - vit bo - - nis, im-
80
bo - nis, [im - ple - vit bo - nis,] im - ple - - vit bo -
bo - nis, im - ple - - vit bo - nis, im - ple - vit
- tes im - ple - vit bo - nis, [im - ple - vit bo-
-ple - vit bo - nis, [im - ple - vit bo - nis:]
85
- nis: et di - vi - tes di - mi - sit in - a - nes, di - mi - sit in - a - -
bo - nis: et di - vi - tes, et di - vi - tes di - mi - sit
- nis:] et di - vi - tes, et di - vi - tes di - mi - sit, et
et di - vi - tes di - mi - sit in - a - nes, et di - vi -
-nes, et di - vi - tes di - mi - sit in - a - nes, et
in - a - nes, in - a - - nes, et di - vi -
di - vi - tes di - mi - sit in - a - nes, di - mi - sit in - a -
- tes di - mi - sit in - a - nes, et di - vi - tes di -

90
di- vi- tes di- mi- - sit in- a- nes, in- a- nes.
- tes di- mi- sit in- - a- nes.
-nes, et di- vi- tes di- mi- sit in- a- nes.
- mi- sit in- a- nes, di- mi- sit in- a- nes.
95
Si- cut lo- cu- tus est, si- -
Si- cut lo- cu- tus est, si- cut lo- cu- tus
Si- cut lo- cu- tus est, si- cut lo- cu-
Si- cut lo- cu-
100
- cut lo- cu- tus est ad pa- tres no- - stros, ad
est ad pa- - tres no- stros, ad pa- tres no- stros, ad pa- tres no-
- tus est ad pa- tres no- stros, ad pa- tres no- stros, ad
- tus est ad pa- tres no- - stros,

105
pa - tres no - - - stros:
- stros, [ad pa - - tres no - stros,] ad pa - tres no - stros: A -
pa - tres no - stros, ad pa - tres no - stros: A - bra -
ad pa - tres no - - stros: A - bra -
110
A - bra - ham et se - mi - ni, et se - mi - ni, et se - mi - ni e - jus in
- bra - ham et se - mi - ni, et se - mi - ni e - jus in sae - cu -
- ham, A - bra - ham et se - mi - ni, et se - mi - ni, et se - mi - ni e -
- ham, A - bra - ham et se - mi - ni, et se - mi - ni, [et se - mi - ni] e -
115
sae - cu - la, in sae - - cu - la, in sae - cu - la.
- la, in sae - - cu - la, in sae - cu - la, in sae - cu - la.
- jus in sae - - cu - la.
- jus in sae - - cu - la, in sae - cu - la.

120
Si - cut e - - rat, si - cut e - rat
Si - - cut e - - rat, si -
Si - - cut e - - rat,
Si - - cut e - - rat, si -
Si - - cut e -
Si - cut e - rat, si - cut
125
in prin - - ci - - pi - o, et
- cut e - - rat in prin -
si - cut e - rat in prin - ci - - pi - o,
- cut e - rat, [si - cut e - rat] in prin -
- - rat in prin - ci - pi - o, in
e - - rat in

130
nunc, et nunc, et sem - - per: et in
- ci - - pi - o, et in
et nunc, et nunc, et sem - per: et in
- ci - pi - o, et nunc, et sem-per, et nunc, et
prin - ci - - pi - o, et nunc, et sem - per: et in
prin - ci - pi - o, et nunc, et sem - - per:
135
sae - cu - la, et in sae - cu - la, et in sae - cu - la sae -
sae - cu - la sae - cu - lo - rum, sae -
sae - cu - la, et in sae - cu - la sae - cu - lo - rum, et in sae - cu - la sae -
sem - per, et nunc, et sem - per: et in sae - cu - la
sae - cu - la, et in sae - cu - la sae - cu - lo - rum, et
et in sae - cu - la sae - cu - lo - rum.

140
-cu-lo- rum. A-men, sae-cu-lo- rum, a-
-cu-lo- -rum. A- men, sae-cu-lo- rum, a-men, sae- cu- lo- rum, a-
-cu-lo- rum, sae- - cu- lo- rum. A-men,
sae-cu-lo- rum. A- men, sae- cu- lo- rum, a- - men,
in sae-cu-la sae-cu-lo- - rum. A- men, sae- - cu-lo-rum,
A- men, sae-cu-lo-rum, a- men,

145
-men.
- men, sae- cu-lo- rum, a- men.
sae- cu-lo- -rum, a- men, a- men.
a- men.
a- men, sae-cu- lo- - rum, a- men.
[sae- cu- lo- rum, a- men.]

Hosanna filio David

20
-nit in no- - mi- ne Do- - mi- ni, qui ve- nit
-di- ctus qui ve- nit in no- mi- ne Do- mi-
- nit in no- - -
- nit, qui ve- nit in no-mi- ne Do- mi-
25
in no- mi- ne Do- - mi- ni. O Rex Is- ra-
-ni, in no- - mi- ne Do-mi- ni. O Rex Is-
-mi- ne Do- mi- ni. O Rex Is-
-ni, in no- mi- ne Do-mi- ni. O Rex Is- ra-
30
-el, o Rex Is- - ra- el: Ho- san- na
- ra- el, o Rex Is- - ra- el: Ho- san- na in ex-
- - ra- el: Ho- san- - na
- el, o Rex Is- - ra- el: Ho- san-
35
in ex- - cel- sis, in ex- cel- sis.
-cel- sis, ho- san- na in ex- cel- sis, in ex- cel- sis.
in ex- cel- sis, in ex- cel- sis.
-na in ex- cel- sis, in ex- - cel- sis.

Pueri Hebraeorum portantes

20
- rum, ra - - mos o - li - va - rum, ob - vi - a - ve - runt
- rum, ob - vi - a - ve - runt Do - - mi - no, ob - vi - a - ve -
- va - rum, ob - vi - a - ve - - runt Do - - mi - no, ob - vi - a - ve -
- rum, ob - vi - a - ve - runt Do - - mi - no,
25
Do - - mi - no, ob - vi - a - ve - runt Do - mi - no, Do -
- runt Do - - mi - no, ob - vi - a - ve - runt Do - mi - no, ob - vi - a - ve - runt
- runt Do - mi - no, ob - vi - a - ve -
ob - vi - a - ve - runt Do - mi - no, ob - vi - a -
30
- - mi - no, cla -
Do - mi - no, cla - man - tes, cla -
- runt Do - - mi - no, cla - man - - tes, cla -
- ve - runt Do - mi - no, cla - man - - - tes,
35
- man - tes, et di - cen -
- man - - tes, cla - man - tes, et di - - cen -
- man - tes, cla - man - tes, et di - cen -
et di - cen - tes:

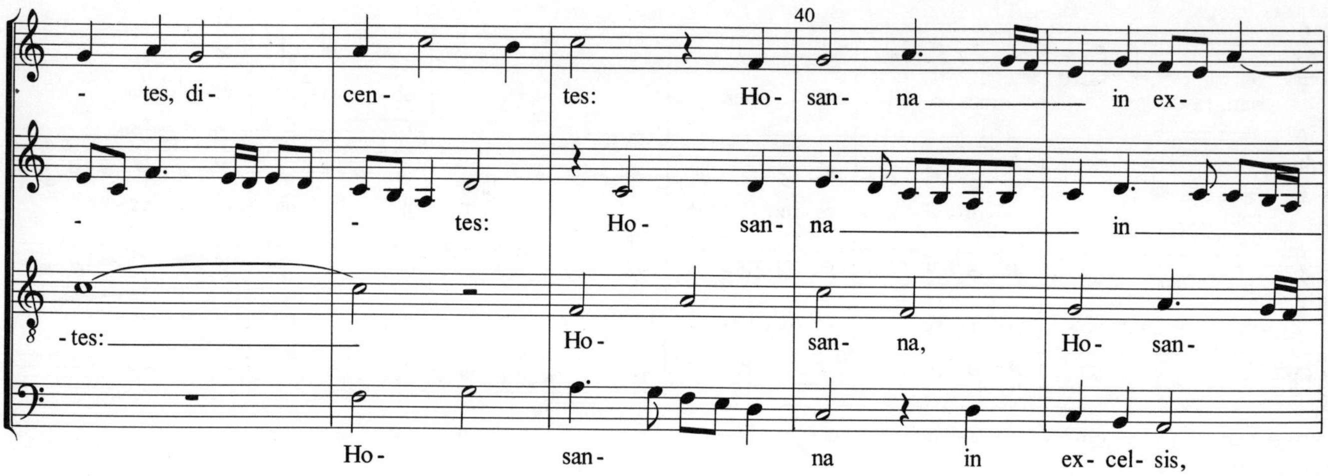

Pueri Hebraeorum vestimenta

10
-sti- men-ta ster- - ne- - bant in vi- - a,
- e-ri He-brae- o- rum ve- sti-men- ta ster- ne- bant
-rum ve- sti- men- ta ster- ne- bant in
- brae- o- - rum ve- sti- men- ta ster- ne- bant
15
et cla-ma- bant, et cla- ma-bant di- cen-
in vi- a, et cla- ma- bant, et cla- ma-bant Ho-
vi- a, et cla- ma- bant di- cen-
in vi- a, et cla-ma- bant, et cla-ma- bant di- cen-
20
-tes: Ho-san- - na fi- - li- o Da- vid: be-
-san- - na fi- li- o Da- - vid:
-tes: Ho- san- na fi- li- o Da-
-tes: Ho- san- - na, Ho- san- na fi- li- o Da- vid:
25
-ne- di- ctus qui ve- nit, qui ve-
be- ne- di- ctus qui ve- - nit, be- ne- di-ctus qui
- vid: be- ne- di- ctus qui ve-
be- ne- di- ctus, be- ne- di- ctus qui ve-

30
-nit in no-mi-ne Do- mi- ni, in no-
ve- nit in no-mi-ne Do- - mi- ni, in no- mi- ne, in
-nit in no- - mi- ne Do- mi- ni,
-nit in no-mi-ne Do- mi- ni,
35
-mi- ne Do-mi-ni, in no- mi- ne
no- mi- ne Do- - mi- ni, in no-mi-ne Do- mi-
in no- mi- ne Do- - mi- ni, in no-mi- ne, in no-
in no- mi- ne Do- mi- ni, in
40
Do- - mi- ni, in no-mi- ne Do- mi- ni.
-ni, in no- mi- ne Do- mi- ni, in no-mi- ne Do- mi- ni.
-mi- ne Do- - mi- ni.
no-mi- ne Do- mi- ni, in no-mi- ne Do- - mi- ni.

Litania de B.V.M.

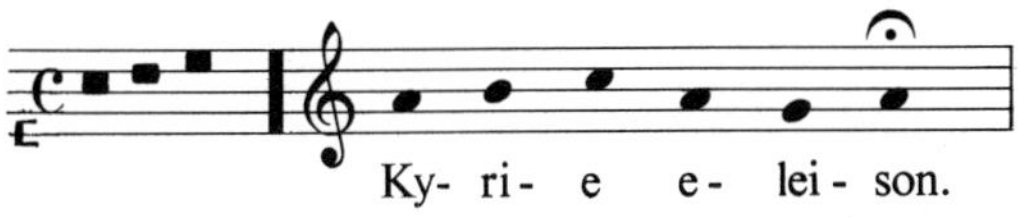

Ky- ri- e e- lei- son.
Ky- ri- e e- lei- - son.
Ky- ri- e e- lei- son.
Ky- ri- e e- lei- son.
Ky- ri- e e- lei- son.
1.Chri - ste au- di nos.
2.Chri - ste ex- au - di nos.
1. Chri - ste au- di nos.
2. Chri - ste ex - au- di nos.
1. Chri- ste au- di nos.
2. Chri- ste ex- au- di nos.
1. Chri - ste au - di nos.
2. Chri - ste ex - au - di nos.
1. Chri- ste au- di nos.
2. Chri- ste ex- au - di nos.
Pa - ter de cae - lis De - us,
Pa- ter de cae- lis De- us, mi- se- re- re no- bis.
Pa- ter de cae- lis De- us, mi- se- re- re no- bis.
Pa- ter de cae- lis De- us, mi- se- re- re no- bis.
Pa- ter de cae- lis De- us, mi- se- re- re no- bis.

Fi- li Re- dem- ptor mun- di De- us,
Fi- li Re- dem-ptor mun-di De- us, mi- se- re- re no- bis.
Fi- li Re- dem-ptor mun-di De- us, mi- se- re- re no- bis.
Fi- li Re- dem-ptor mun-di De- us, mi- se- re- re no- bis.
Fi- li Re- dem-ptor mun-di De- us, mi- se- re- re no- bis.
Spi- ri- tus San- cte De- us,
Spi- ri- tus San-cte De- us, mi- se- re- re no- bis.
Spi- ri- tus San-cte De- us, mi- se- re- re no- bis.
Spi- ri- tus San-cte De- us, mi- se- re- re no- bis.
Spi- ri- tus San-cte De- us, mi- se- re- re no- bis.
San- cta Tri- ni- tas, u- nus De- us,
San- cta Tri- ni- tas, u- nus De- us, mi- se- re- re no- bis.
San- cta Tri- ni- tas, u- nus De- us, mi- se- re- re no- bis.
San- cta Tri- ni- tas, u- nus De- us, mi- se- re- re no- bis.
San- cta Tri- ni- tas, u- nus De- us, mi- se- re- re no- bis.

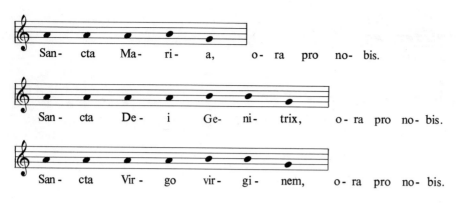

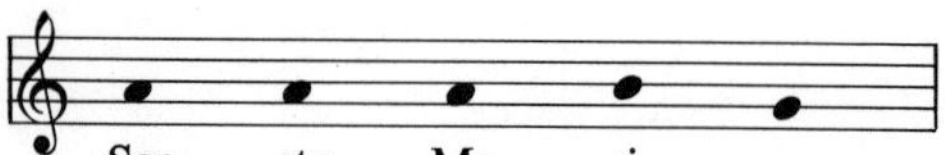
San- cta Ma- ri- a, o- ra pro no- bis.

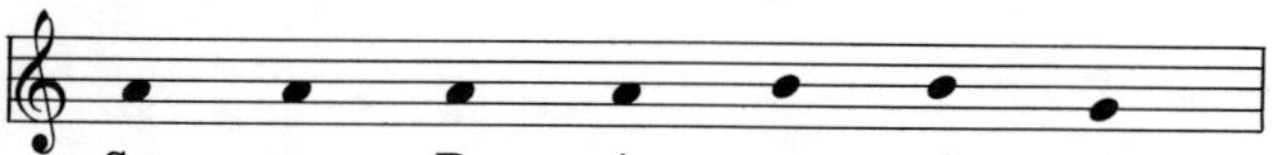
San - cta De - i Ge- ni- trix, o- ra pro no- bis.

San - cta Vir - go vir - gi - nem, o- ra pro no- bis.

Ma-ter Chri-sti, o-ra pro no-bis.
Ma-ter di-vi-nae gra-ti-ae, o-ra pro no-bis.
Ma-ter pu-ris-si-ma, o-ra pro no-bis.
Ma-ter ca-stis-si-ma, o-ra pro no-bis.
Ma-ter in-vi-o-la-ta, o-ra pro no-bis.
Ma-ter in-te-me-ra-ta, o-ra pro no-bis.
Ma-ter a-ma-bi-lis, o-ra pro no-bis,
Ma-ter ad-mi-ra-bi-lis, o-ra pro no-bis.
Ma-ter Cre-a-to-ris, o-ra pro no-bis.
Ma-ter Sal-va-to-ris, o-ra pro no-bis.
Vir-go pru-den-tis-si-ma, o-ra pro no-bis.
Vir-go ve-ne-ran-da, o-ra pro no-bis.
Vir-go prae-di-can-da, o-ra pro no-bis.
Vir-go po-tens, o-ra pro no-bis.
Vir-go cle-mens, o-ra pro no-bis.
Vir-go fi-de-lis, o-ra pro no-bis.
Spe-cu-lum ju-sti-ti-ae, o-ra pro no-bis.
Se-des sa-pi-en-ti-ae, o-ra pro no-bis.
Cau-sa no-strae lae-ti-ti-ae, o-ra pro no-bis.
Vas spi-ri-tu-a-le, o-ra pro no-bis.
Vas ho-no-ra-bi-le, o-ra pro no-bis.
Vas in-si-gne de-vo-ti-o-nis, o-ra pro no-bis.
Ro-sa my-sti-ca, o-ra pro no-bis.
Tur-ris Da-vi-di-ca, o-ra pro no-bis.
Tur-ris e-bur-ne-a, o-ra pro no-bis.
Do-mus au-re-a, o-ra pro no-bis.
Foe-de-ris ar-ca, o-ra pro no-bis.
Ja-nu-a cae-li, o-ra pro no-bis.
Stel-la ma-tu-ti-na, o-ra pro no-bis.
Sa-lus in-fir-mo-rum, o-ra pro no-bis.
Re-fu-gi-um pec-ca-to-rum, o-ra pro no-bis.
Con-so-la-trix af-fli-cto-rum, o-ra pro no-bis.
Au-xi-li-um Chri-sti-a-no-rum, o-ra pro no-bis.
Re-gi-na An-ge-lo-rum, o-ra pro no-bis.
Re-gi-na Pa-tri-ar-cha-rum, o-ra pro no-bis.
Re-gi-na Pro-phe-ta-rum, o-ra pro nobis.
Re-gi-na A-po-sto-lo-rum, o-ra pro no-bis.
Re-gi-na Mar-ty-rum, o-ra pro no-bis.
Re-gi-na Con-fes-so-rum, o-ra pro no-bis.
Re-gi-na Vir-gi-num, o-ra pro no-bis.
Re-gi-na San-cto-rum om-ni-um, o-ra pro no-bis.

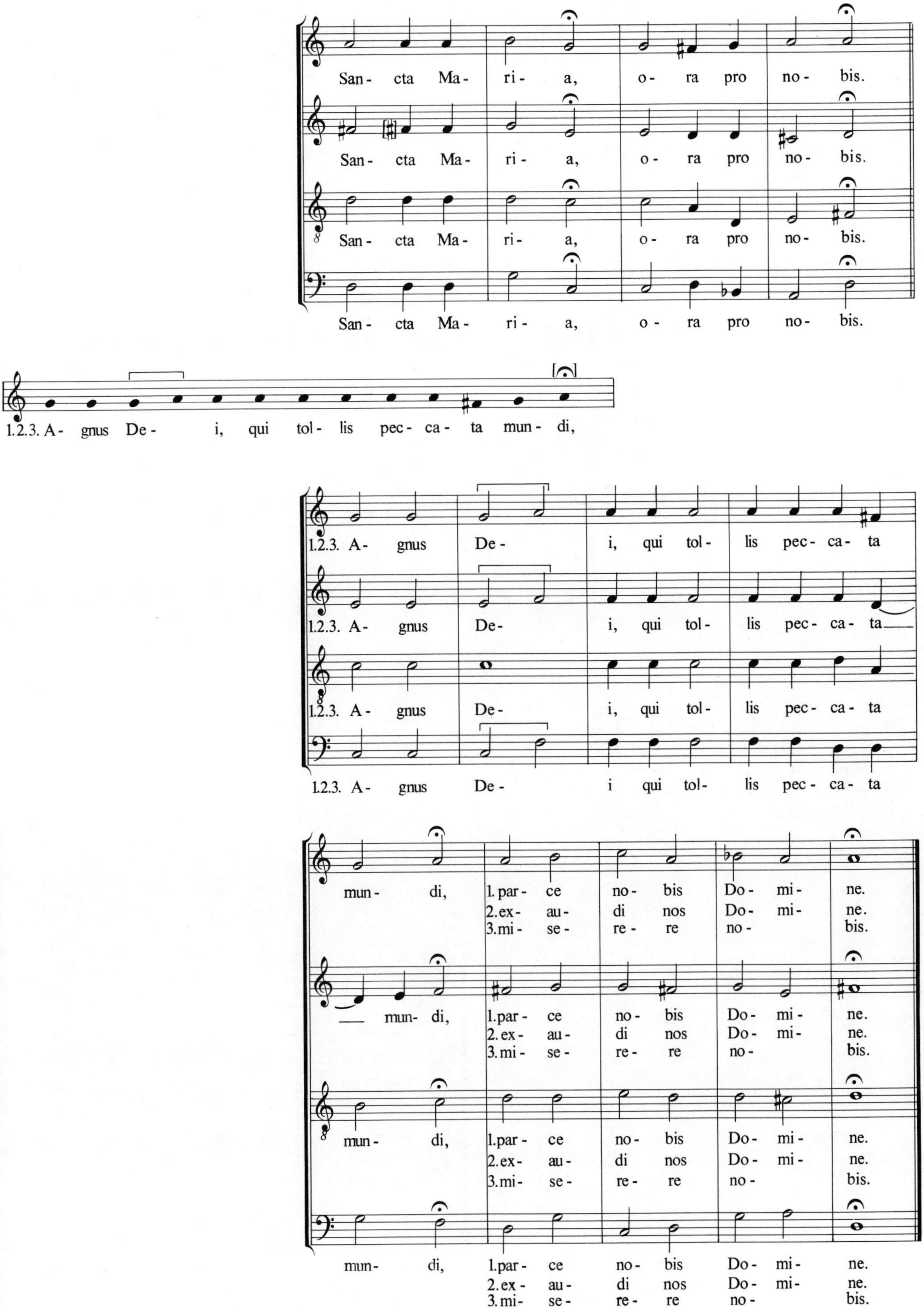
San- cta Ma- ri- a, o- ra pro no- bis.
San- cta Ma- ri- a, o- ra pro no- bis.
San- cta Ma- ri- a, o- ra pro no- bis.
San- cta Ma- ri- a, o- ra pro no- bis.
1.2.3. A- gnus De- i, qui tol- lis pec- ca- ta mun- di,
1.2.3. A- gnus De- i, qui tol- lis pec- ca- ta
1.2.3. A- gnus De- i, qui tol- lis pec- ca- ta
1.2.3. A- gnus De- i, qui tol- lis pec- ca- ta
1.2.3. A- gnus De- i qui tol- lis pec- ca- ta
mun- di, 1. par- ce no- bis Do- mi- ne.
2. ex- au- di nos Do- mi- ne.
3. mi- se- re- re no- bis.
mun- di, 1. par- ce no- bis Do- mi- ne.
2. ex- au- di nos Do- mi- ne.
3. mi- se- re- re no- bis.
mun- di, 1. par- ce no- bis Do- mi- ne.
2. ex- au- di nos Do- mi- ne.
3. mi- se- re- re no- bis.
mun- di, 1. par- ce no- bis Do- mi- ne.
2. ex- au- di nos Do- mi- ne.
3. mi- se- re- re no- bis.

Litania de B.V.M.

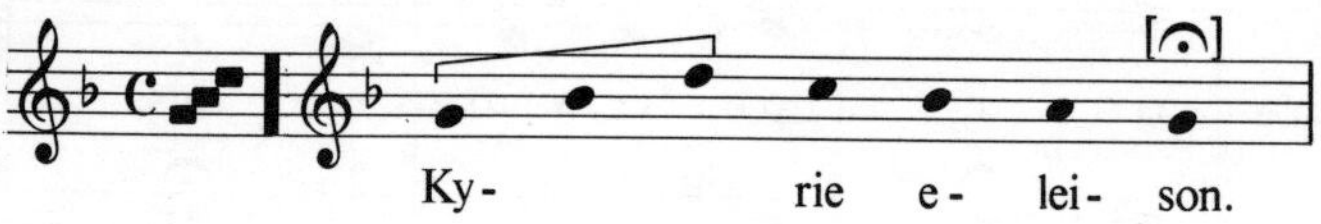

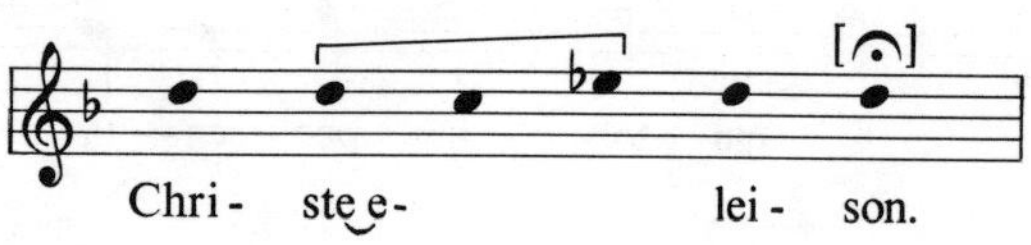

Ky- ri- e e- lei- son.

Ky- ri- e e- lei- son.
Ky- ri- e e- lei- son.
Ky- ri- e e- lei- son.
Ky- ri- e e- lei- son.

1. Chri- ste au- di nos.
2. Chri- ste ex- au- di nos.

1. Chri- ste au- - di nos.
2. Chri- ste ex- - au- di nos.
1. Chri- ste au- di nos.
2. Chri- ste ex- au-di nos.
1. Chri- ste au- di nos.
2. Chri- ste ex- au- di nos.
1. Chri- ste au- di nos.
2. Chri- ste ex- au-di nos.

Pa- ter de cae- lis De- us, mi- se- re- re no- bis.
Fi- li Re- dem- ptor mun- di De- us, mi- se- re- re no- bis.
Spi- ri- tus San- cte De- us, mi- se- re- re no- bis.
San- cta Tri- ni- tas, u- nus De- us, mi- se- re- re no- bis.

San-cta De-i Ge-ni-trix, o-ra pro no-bis.
San-cta Vir-go vir-gi-num, o-ra pro no-bis.
Ma-ter Chri-sti, o-ra pro no-bis.
Ma-ter di-vi-nae gra-ti-ae, o-ra pro no-bis.
Ma-ter pu-ris-si-ma, o-ra pro no-bis.
Ma-ter ca-stis-si-ma, o-ra pro no-bis.
Ma-ter in-vi-o-la-ta, o-ra pro no-bis.
Ma-ter in-te-me-ra-ta, o-ra pro no-bis.
Ma-ter a-ma-bi-lis, o-ra pro no-bis.
Ma-ter ad-mi-ra-bi-lis, o-ra pro no-bis.
Ma-ter Cre-a-to-ris, o-ra pro no-bis.
Ma-ter Sal-va-to-ris, o-ra pro no-bis.
Vir-go pru-den-tis-si-ma, o-ra pro no-bis.
Vir-go ve-ne-ran-da, o-ra pro no-bis.
Vir-go prae-di-can-da, o-ra pro no-bis.
Vir-go po-tens, o-ra pro no-bis.
Vir-go cle-mens, o-ra pro no-bis.
Vir-go fi-de-lis, o-ra pro no-bis.
Spe-cu-lum ju-sti-ti-ae, o-ra pro no-bis.
Se-des sa-pi-en-ti-ae, o-ra pro no-bis.
Cau-sa no-strae lae-ti-ti-ae, o-ra pro no-bis.
Vas spi-ri-tu-a-le, o-ra pro no-bis.
Vas ho-no-ra-bi-le, o-ra pro no-bis.
Vas in-si-gne de-vo-ti-o-nis, o-ra pro no-bis.
Ro-sa my-sti-ca, o-ra pro no-bis.
Tur-ris Da-vi-di-ca, o-ra pro no-bis.
Tur-ris e-bur-ne-a, o-ra pro no-bis.
Do-mus au-re-a, o-ra pro no-bis.
Foe-de-ris ar-ca, o-ra pro no-bis.
Ja-nu-a cae-li, o-ra pro no-bis.
Stel-la ma-tu-ti-na, o-ra pro no-bis.
Sa-lus in-fir-mo-rum, o-ra pro no-bis.
Re-fu-gi-um pec-ca-to-rum, o-ra pro no-bis.
Con-so-la-trix af-fli-cto-rum, o-ra pro no-bis.
Au-xi-li-um Chri-sti-a-no-rum, o-ra pro no-bis.
Re-gi-na An-ge-lo-rum, o-ra pro no-bis.
Re-gi-na Pa-tri-ar-cha-rum, o-ra pro no-bis.
Re-gi-na Pro-phe-ta-rum, o-ra pro no-bis.
Re-gi-na A-po-sto-lo-rum, o-ra pro no-bis.

Re-gi-na Mar-ty-rum, o-ra pro no-bis.
Re-gi-na Con-fes-so-rum, o-ra pro no-bis.
Re-gi-na Vir-gi-num, o-ra pro no-bis.
Re-gi-na San-cto-rum om-ni-um, o-ra pro no-bis.

Stabat mater

A.4. C.A.T.B.

15
dum pen- de- bat fi- li- us, cu- jus a- - ni- mam ge- men- tem
dum pen- de- bat fi- li- us, cu- jus a- - ni- mam ge- men- tem
dum pen- de- bat fi- li- us, cu- jus a- - ni- mam ge- men- tem
dum pen- de- bat fi- li- us, cu- jus a- - ni- mam ge- men- tem
20
25
con- tri- stan- tem et do- len- tem, per- tran- si- vit gla- di- us.
con- tri- stan- tem et do- len- tem, per- tran- si- vit gla- di- us.
con- tri- stan- tem et do- len- tem, per- tran- si- vit gla- di- us.
con- tri- stan- tem et do- len- tem, per- tran- si- vit gla- di- us.

30
O quam tri- stis et af- fli- cta fu- it il- la be- ne- di- cta ma- ter
O quam tri- stis et af- fli- cta fu- it il- la be- ne- di- cta ma- ter
O quam tri- stis et af- fli- cta ma- ter
O quam tri- stis et af- fli- cta ma- ter
35
40
u- ni- ge- ni- ti. Quae mae- re- bat et do- le- bat et tre- me-
u- ni- ge- ni- ti. Quae mae- re- bat et do- le- bat et tre- me-
u- ni- ge- ni- ti. Quae mae- re- bat et do- le- - bat et tre- me-
u- ni- ge- ni- ti. Quae mae- re- bat et do- le- bat et tre- me-

45
-bat cum vi- de- bat. Na- ti poe- nas in- cly- ti. Quis est ho- mo qui
-bat cum vi- de- bat. Na- ti poe- nas in- cly- ti. Quis est ho- mo qui
-bat cum vi- de- - bat. Na- ti poe- nas in- cly- ti. Quis est ho- mo qui
-bat cum vi- de- bat. Na- ti poe- nas in- cly- ti. Quis est ho- mo qui
4 3
50
55
non fle- ret, Chri- sti ma- trem si vi- de- ret in tan- to sup- pli- ci-
non fle- ret, Chri- sti ma- trem si vi- de- ret in tan- to sup- pli- ci-
non fle- ret, Chri- sti ma- trem si vi- de- ret in tan- to sup- pli- ci-
non fle- ret, Chri- sti ma- trem si vi- de- ret in tan- to sup- pli- ci-
6

60
65
-o. Quis non pos- sit con- tri- sta- ri, pi- am ma- trem con- tem- pla- ri,
-o. Quis non pos- sit con- tri- sta- ri, pi- am ma- trem con- tem- pla- ri,
-o. Quis non pos- sit con- tri- sta- ri, pi- am ma- trem con- tem- pla- ri,
-o. Quis non pos- sit con- tri- sta- ri, pi- am ma- trem con- tem- pla- ri,

70
75
do- len- tem cum fi- li- o. Pro pec- ca- tis su- ae gen- tis, vi- dit Je-
do- len- tem cum fi- li- o. Pro pec- ca- tis su- ae gen- tis, vi- dit Je-
do- len- tem cum fi- li- o. Pro pec- ca- tis su- ae gen- tis, vi- dit Je-
do- len- tem cum fi- li- o. Pro pec- ca- tis su- ae gen- tis, vi- dit Je-

80
85
-sum in tor-men-tis et fla-gel-lis sub-di-tum, vi-dit su-um dul-
90
-cem na-tum, mo-ri-en-tem de-so-la-tum, dum e-mi-sit Spi-ri-tum.

95
100
E - ja ma - ter fons a - mo - ris me sen - ti - re vim
E - ja ma - ter fons a - mo - ris me sen - ti -
E - ja ma - ter fons a - mo - ris me sen - ti -
E - ja ma - ter fons a - mo - ris me sen - ti - re vim
105
do - lo - ris fac ut te - cum lu - ge - am.
-re vim do - lo - ris fac ut te - cum lu - ge - am.
-re vim do - lo - ris fac ut te - cum lu - ge - am.
do - lo - ris fac ut te - cum lu - ge - am.

110
Fac ut ar - de - at cor me - um in a - man - do Chri - stum De -
Fac ut ar - de - at cor me - um in a - man - do Chri - stum De -
Fac ut ar - de - at cor me - um in a - man - do Chri - stum De -
Fac ut ar - de - at cor me - um in a - man - do Chri - stum De -
115
-um, ut si - bi com- pla - ce- am. San-cta Ma - - ter i -
-um, ut si - bi com- pla - ce- am. i -
-um, ut si - bi com- pla - ce- am. San - cta Ma-ter i -
-um, ut si - bi com- pla - ce- am. San-cta Ma - ter i -

120
-stud a- gas cru- ci- fi- xi fi- ge pla- gas
-stud a- gas cru- ci- fi- - xi fi- ge pla - gas
-stud a- gas cru- ci- fi- xi fi- ge pla- gas
-stud a- gas cru- ci- fi- xi fi- ge pla- gas
6 5 6 5 6 5 6 5 7 6

125
130
cor- di me- o va- li- de. Tu- i na- ti vul- ne- ra- ti,
cor- di me- o va- li- de. Tu- i na- ti vul- ne- ra- ti,
cor- di me- o va- li- de. Tu- i na- ti vul- ne- ra- ti,
cor- di me- o va- li- de. Tu- i na- ti vul- ne- ra- ti,

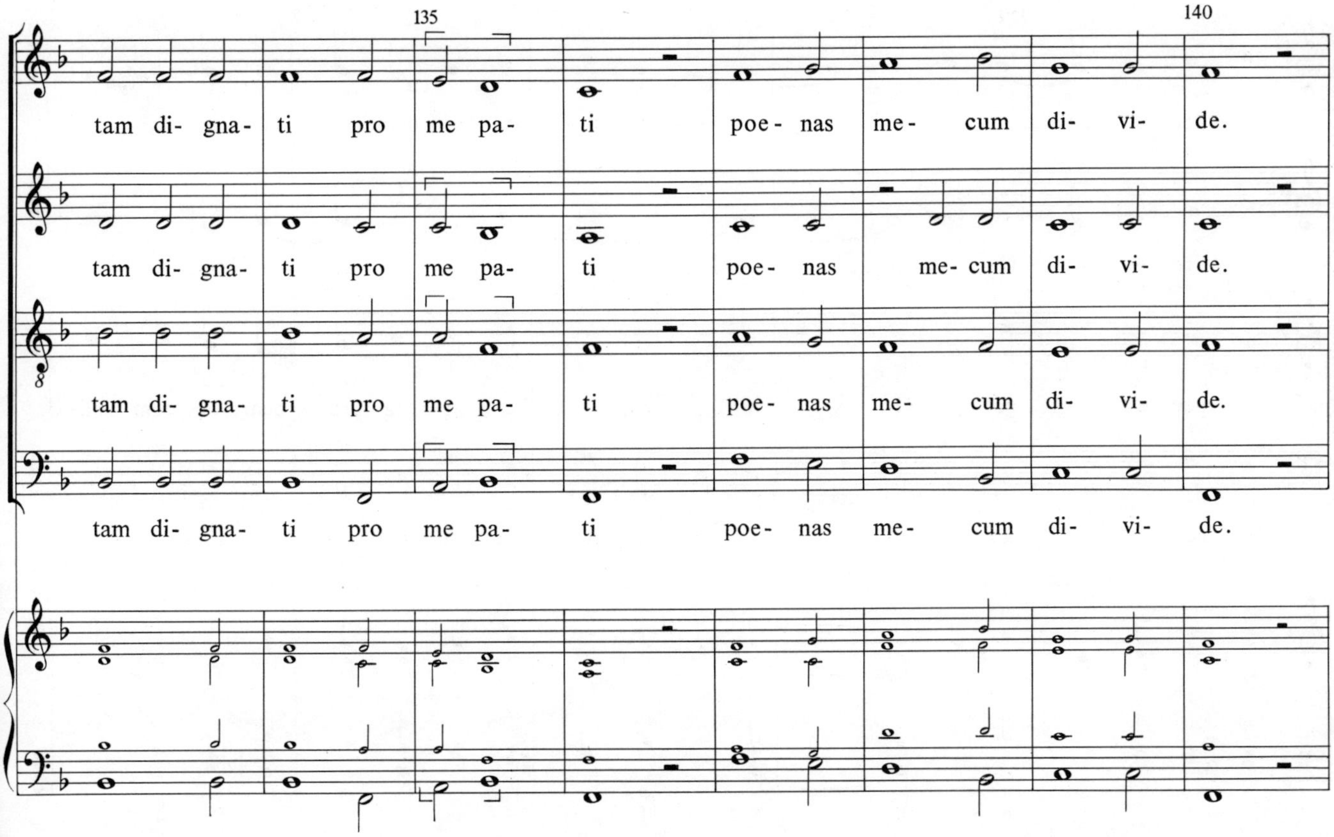
135
140
tam di- gna- ti pro me pa- ti poe- nas me- cum di- vi- de.
tam di- gna- ti pro me pa- ti poe- nas me- cum di- vi- de.
tam di- gna- ti pro me pa- ti poe- nas me- cum di- vi- de.
tam di- gna- ti pro me pa- ti poe- nas me- cum di- vi- de.

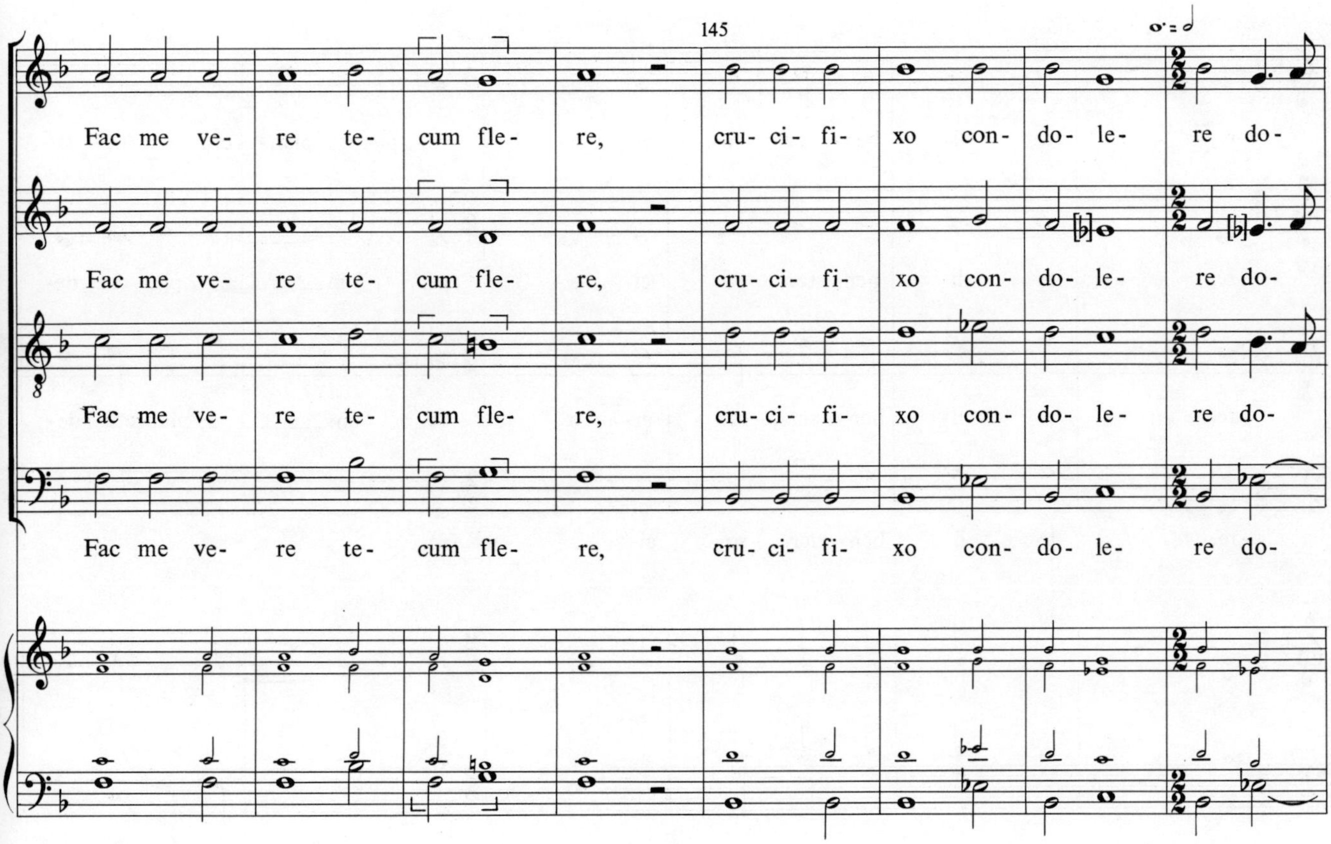
145
Fac me ve- re te- cum fle- re, cru- ci- fi- xo con- do- le- re do-
Fac me ve- re te- cum fle- re, cru- ci- fi- xo con- do- le- re do-
Fac me ve- re te- cum fle- re, cru- ci- fi- xo con- do- le- re do-
Fac me ve- re te- cum fle- re, cru- ci- fi- xo con- do- le- re do-

150
- nec e- go vi- - xe- ro, ju- xta cru- cem te- cum sta-
- nec e- go vi- xe- ro, te- - cum sta-
- nec e- go vi- xe- ro, ju- xta cru- cem te- cum sta-
- nec e- go vi- - xe- ro, ju- xta cru- cem te- cum sta-
155
-re, te li- ben- ter so- ci- a- re, in plan- ctu de- si-
-re, te li- ben- ter so- ci- a- re, in plan-ctu de-
-re, te li- ben- ter so- ci- a- re, in plan-ctu de-
-re, te li- ben- ter so- ci- a- re,

* In the source these two figures are given in the reverse order.

Adiuro vos

A.4. Duo Can. vel Ten. et 2. Bassi

10
nunc - i - e - tis e - i, ut nunc - i - e - tis e - i qui - a a - mo - re lan - gue -
- i, ut nunc - i - e - tis e - i qui - a a - mo - re lan - gue -
15
- o.
Qua - lis est di - le - ctus tu - us ex di - le - cto o
- o.
Qua - lis est di - le - ctus tu - us ex di - le - cto o o

20
o o pul-cher-ri-ma mu-li-e-rum. Qua-lis est di-le-ctus tu-us ex
o o pul-cher-ri-ma mu-li-e-rum. Qua-lis est di-le-ctus tu-us ex di-
Di-le-ctus me-us can-di-dus
di-le-cto qui-a sic a-diu-ra-sti nos ?
Di-le-ctus me-us can-di-dus
-le-cto qui-a sic a-dui-ra-sti nos ?

25
et ru-bi-cun-dus, e-le - ctus, e - le - ctus ex mil - - li-bus,
Quo
et ru-bi-cun-dus, e-le-ctus, e-le - ctus ex mil - - li-bus,
Quo
30
a - bi - it di - le - ctus tu - us? Quo a - bi - it, quo a - bi - it o pul-
a - bi - it di - le - ctus tu - us? Quo a - bi - it o pul-cher-ri -
(♭)

-cher - ri - ma , o pul - cher - ri - ma mu - li - e - rum quo a - bi - it ?
- ma , o pul - cher - ri - ma mu - li - e - rum quo a - bi - it ? Di -
35
et quae - re -
Di - le - ctus tu - us can - di - dus et ru - bi - cun - dus ,
et quae - re -
- le - ctus tu - us can - di - dus et ru - bi - cun - dus ,

40
- mus e - um, et quae-re - - mus e - um de-scen -
et quae-re - - mus e - um, quae- re - mus e - um de -
- mus e - um, et quae-re - - mus e - um,
et quae-re - - mus e - um, quae- re - mus e - um de -
- dit in hor - tum me - um, de - scen - dit in hor - tum me - um,
- scen - dit in hor - tum me - um, de - scen - dit in hor - tum me -
de - scen - dit in hor - tum me - um, de - scen -
- scen - dit in hor - tum me - um, de - scen - dit, in hor - tum
6

* in the source

Veni dilecte mi

A.4. Duo Can. Ten. et Bass

5
ve- ni, ve- ni, ve- ni, ve- ni, ve- ni, ve- ni, ve- ni, ve-
ve- ni di- le- - cta me- a, ve- ni, ve- ni, ve- ni, ve- ni, ve- ni, ve- ni, ve- ni, ve- ni
ve- ni, ve- ni, ve- ni, ve- ni, ve- ni, ve-
ve- ni, ve- ni, di- le- cta me- a, ve- ni, ve- ni, ve- ni, ve- ni, ve- ni,
10
-ni di- le- cte mi, ve- ni di- le- cta me- a, e- gre- di- a- mur,
di- le- cta me- a, ve- ni, ve- ni di- le- cta me- a, e- gre- di- a-
-ni di- le- cte mi, ve- ni di- le- cta me- a, e- gre- di- a- mur,
ve- ni, ve- ni, ve- ni, di- le- cta me- a, e- gre- di- a-

15
e-gre-di-a- mur in a- grum, e- gre-di- a- mur in a- grum, e-
-mur, e-gre-di- a- mur, e- gre-di- a- mur, e-
e-gre-di- a- mur in a- grum e- gre-di- a- mur in a- grum, e-
-mur, e- gre-di- a- mur, e- gre-di- a- mur, e-
-gre-di- a- mur in a- grum, vi-de-a- mus si flo- ru-it, si
-gre-di- a- mur in a- grum, vi-de-a- mus si flo- ru-
-gre-di- a- mur in a- grum, vi-de-a- mus si flo- ru-it, si
-gre-di- a- mur in a- grum, vi-de-a- mus si flo- ru-

20
flo- ru-it vi- ne- a,
com-mo-re-mur in vil-
-it,
si flo-ru-it vi- ne- a,com-mo-re- mur in vil- lis,
flo- ru-it vi- ne- a,
com-mo-re- mur in vil-
-it,
si flo-ru-it vi- ne- a,com-mo-re- mur in vil- lis,
25
-lis,ma-ne sur-ga- mus,ma- ne sur-ga- mus ad vi- ne- as.
ma-ne sur-ga- mus,ma- ne sur-ga- mus ad vi-
-lis,ma-ne sur-ga- mus,ma- ne sur-ga- mus ad vi- ne- as.
ma-ne sur-ga- mus,ma- ne sur-ga- mus ad vi-

30
Vi- de- bi- mus si flo- res fru- ctus par-tu- ri-runt,
- ne-as. Vi- de-bi- mus si flo- res fru-
Vi- de- bi- mus si flo- res fru- ctus par-tu- ri-runt,
- ne- as. Vi- de-bi- mus si flo- res fru-
35
si flo-ru-e- runt ma- la pu- ni-ca,
-ctus par-tu- ri-runt, si flo-ru- e- runt ma- la pu- ni-
si flo- ru-e- runt ma- la pu- ni-ca,
-ctus par-tu- ri-runt, si flo-ru- e- runt ma- la pu- ni-

si flo- ru-e- runt ma- la pu-ni-ca.
-ca, si flo-ru- e- runt ma- la pu- ni-ca. I- - bi da-bo ti- bi u- be-ra me-
[si flo- ru-e- runt ma- la pu- ni-ca.]
-ca, si flo- ru-e- runt ma- la pu-ni-ca. I- - bi da-bo ti- bi u- be-ra me-
40
I- bi da- bo ti- bi u- be- ra me- a, i- - bi da- bo ti- bi
-a, i- - bi da- bo ti- bi
I- bi da- bo ti- bi u- be- ra me- a, i- - bi da- bo ti- bi
- a, i- - bi da- bo ti- bi

45
u- be-ra me- a, i- bi da-bo ti- bi u- be- ra me- a.
u- be-ra me- a, i- bi da-bo ti- bi u- be- ra me- a. Al- le- lu-
u- be-ra me- a, i- bi da-bo ti- bi u- be- ra me- a.
u- be-ra me- a, i- bi da-bo ti- bi u- be- ra me- a. Al- le- lu-
50
Al- le- lu- ia, al- le- lu- ia, al- le- lu-
-ia, al- le- lu- ia, al- le- lu- ia, al- le- lu- ia,
Al- le- lu- ia, al- le- lu- ia, al- le- lu-
-ia, al- le- lu- ia, al- le- lu- ia, al- le- lu- ia,

Petrus Apostolus

A.4. C.A.T.B.

5
Et Pau- lus Do- ctor ge- ni- tum,
i- psi nos do- - cu-e- runt,
i-
10
i- psi- nos do- - cu- e- runt,
-psi nos do- cu- e- runt,
i- psi nos do- cu- e-

* These parallels are in the source.

30
35
le- gem tu- am Do- mi- ne. Pe- tre, Pe- tre
le- gem tu- am Do- mi- ne. Pe- tre ti- - bi tra- di- tae sunt,
le- gem tu- am Do- mi- ne. Pe- tre ti- bi tra- di- tae sunt,
le- gem tu- am Do- mi- ne. Pe- tre,
40
ti- bi tra- di- tae sunt, Pet- re ti- - bi tra- di- tae sunt, Pe-
ti- - bi tra- di- tae sunt, Pe- tre, Pe- tre
Pe- tre ti- bi tra- di- tae sunt,
Pe- tre,

45
-tre ti- bi tra-di- tae sunt cla- ves re- gni cae- lo- -
ti- bi tra- di- tae sunt cla- ves re - gni cae- lo-
ti- bi tra-di- tae sunt cla- ves re- gni cae-lo- rum, re-gni cae-
Pe - tre.
50
- rum. I- de- o di- co ti- bi qui- a. Tu es
- rum. I - de- o di- co ti- bi qui - a.
-lo- rum. I- de- o di- co ti- bi qui- a.
I- de- o di- co ti- bi qui- a.

55
Pe- trus,
Tu es Pe- trus,
Tu es Pe- trus,
Tu
60
et su- per hanc pe-tram ae- di- fi- ca- bo Ec-
et su- per hanc pe- tram
et su- per hanc pe- tram ae- di- fi- ca-
es Pe- trus, et su- per hanc pe- tram

65
-cle- si-am me-am, ae- di- fi- ca- bo Ec- cle- si- am me- am.
ae- di- fi- ca- bo, ae- di- fi- ca- bo Ec- cle- si-am me- am.
-bo, ae- di- fi- ca- bo Ec- cle- si- am me- am.
ae- di- fi- ca- bo Ec- cle- si- am me- am.
70
Et por- tae in- fe- ri non prae-va- le- bunt, et por-tae in- fe- ri non
Et por- tae in- fe- ri non prae-va- le- bunt, et por-tae in- fe- ri non
Et por- tae in- fe- ri non prae-va- le- bunt, et por- tae in- fe- ri non
Et por- tae in- fe- ri non prae-va- le- bunt, et por-tae in- fe- ri non

prae- va- le- bunt, ad- ver- sus e- am. Et por- tae in- fe-
prae- va- le- bunt, ad- ver- sus e- am. Et por- tae in- fe-
prae- va- le- bunt, ad- ver- sus e- am. Et por- tae in- fe-
prae- va- le- bunt, ad- ver- sus e- am. Et por- tae in- fe-
75
-ri non prae- va- le- bunt, ad- ver- sus e- am, ad- ver- sus e- am.
-ri non prae- va- le- bunt, ad- ver- sus e- am, ad- ver- sus e- am.
-ri non prae- va- le- bunt, ad- ver- sus e- am, ad- ver- sus e- am.
-ri non prae- va- le- bunt, ad- ver- sus e- am, ad- ver- sus e- am.

Missus est Angelus

A.4. 2C.T.B. In Dialogo

10
15
A - ve gra- - ti- a ple- na: Do-
-lus ad e- am di- xit:
-lus ad e- am di- xit:
-lus ad e- am di- xit:
4 3
- mi- nus te- cum: Be- ne- di- cta tu in mu- li- e-
4 3
20
- ri- bus.
Quae cum au- dis- set, tur- ba- ta est in ser- mo- ne
Quae cum au- dis- set, tur- ba- ta est in ser- mo- ne e-
Quae cum au- dis- set tur- ba- ta est in ser- mo- ne e-
4 3
7 6
7 6

25
e- ius, et co-gi- ta- bat qua- - lis es- set i- sta sa- lu- ta- ti-
- ius, et co-gi- ta- bat qua- - lis es- set i- sta sa- lu- ta- ti-
- ius, et co-gi- ta- bat qua- - lis es- set i- sta sa- lu- ta- ti-
4 3♯
30
Ne ti- me- as Ma-
-o. Et a- it An- ge- lus e- - i:
-o. Et a- it An- ge- lus e- - i:
-o. Et a- it An- ge- lus e- - i:

35
-ri- a, in- ve- ni- sti e- nim gra- ti-am a- pud
40
De- - um: ec- ce con- ci- pi- es et pa- ri-
43
45
-es fi- li-um, et vo-ca-bis no-men e- ius Je- sum.
Di-xit au-
Di-xit au-
Di-xit au-

50
Di- xit au- tem Ma-
-tem Ma- ri- a ad An- ge- lum:
-tem Ma- ri- a ad An- ge- lum, di- xit au- tem Ma-
-tem Ma- ri- a ad An- ge- lum, di- xit au- tem Ma-
55
-ri- a ad An- ge- lum:
Quo- mo- do fi- - et i-
-ri- a ad An- - ge- lum:
-ri- a ad An- ge- lum:

60
-stud, quo- - ni-am vi- rum non co-gno- sco, non co- gno-
- sco?
65
Et re-spon-dens An- ge-lus di-xit e- - i:
Et
Et re-spon-dens An- ge-lus di- - xit e- - i. Et
Et re-spon-den-dens An- ge-lus di- - xit e- - i. Et
3 4
70
Spi- ri-tus san-ctus su-per-ve- ni-
re-spon-dens An- ge-lus di- xit e- i:
re-spon-dens An- ge-lus di- - xit e- i:
re-spon-dens An- ge-lus di- - xit e- i:
7 6

75
-et, su-per-ve-ni-et in te, et vir-tus Al- tis- si- mi o- -brum-bra-
80
- bit ti- bi. I- de- o- que et quod na-sce-tur ex te San-ctum, vo-
-ca- bi-tur, vo-ca- bi- tur Fi- li-us De- i.
Di- xit au- tem Ma- ri-
Di- xit au- tem Ma-ri-
Di- xit au- tem Ma- ri-

Di- xit au- tem Ma-ri- - a:
- a:
Ec- ce an- cil- la Do- mi- ni,
- a, di- xit au- tem Ma- ri- - a:
- a, di- xit au- tem Ma- ri- - a:
Ec- ce an- cil- la Do- mi- ni, fi- at mi- hi
fi- at mi- hi se - cun - dum
Ec- ce an- cil- la Do- mi- ni, fi- at mi- hi
Ec- ce an- cil- la Do- mi- ni, fi- at mi- hi

100
105
se - cun - dum ver - bum tu - um,
ver - bum tu - um. Ec - ce an - cil - la
se - cun - dum ver - bum tu - um,
se - cun - dum ver - bum tu - um,

110
115
fi - at mi - hi Ec - ce an - cil - la
Do - mi - ni, se - cun - dum ver - bum tu - um. Ec - ce an - cil - la
fi - at mi - hi Ec - ce an - cil - la
fi - at mi - hi Ec - ce an - cil - la

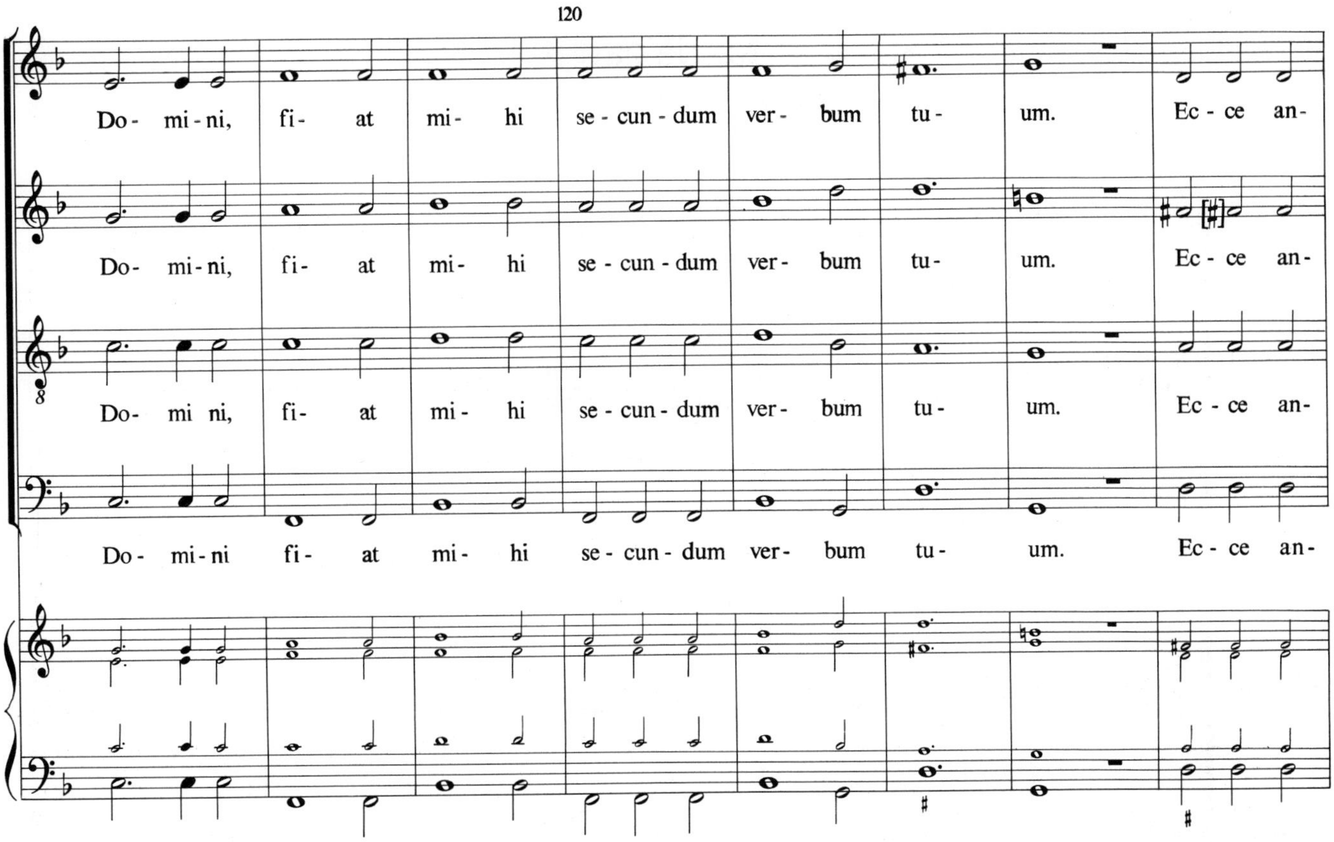
120
Do- mi-ni, fi- at mi- hi se-cun-dum ver- bum tu- um. Ec-ce an-
Do- mi-ni, fi- at mi- hi se-cun-dum ver- bum tu- um. Ec-ce an-
Do- mi ni, fi- at mi- hi se-cun-dum ver- bum tu- um. Ec-ce an-
Do- mi-ni fi- at mi- hi se-cun-dum ver- bum tu- um. Ec-ce an-

125
130
-cil- la Do- mi-ni, fi- at mi- hi se-cun-dum ver- bum tu- um.
-cil- la Do- mi-ni, fi- at mi- hi se-cun-dum ver- bum tu- um.
-cil- la Do- mi-ni, fi- at mi- hi se-cun-dum ver- bum tu- um.
-cil- la Do- mi-ni, fi- at mi- hi se-cun-dum ver- bum tu- um.

Maria zart

* Spelling in the source: ross.

15
hast aus- macht haer - wi - der bracht dass vor - lang ward ver - lo -
- macht haer- wi - der - bracht dass vor - lang ward ver - lo - ren, ward ver - lo -
- macht haer - wi - - der - bracht dass vor - lang ward ver - lo -
- wi - der bracht, haer - wi - der - bracht dass vor - lang, dass vor - lang ward ver - lo -
- macht dass vor - lang ward ver - lo - - ren
- ren, ver - lo - - ren durch A - dams fall, durch A -
- ren durch A - dams fall. Dir hat die wal, dir
- ren durch A - - dams fall. Dir hat
- ren durch A - dams fall. Dir hat die wal, dir hat die wal
durch A - dams fall. Dir hat die wal, durch A - dams
20
- dams fall. Dir hat die wal Sanct Ga - bri - el ver -
hat die wal, dir hat die wal Sanct Ga - bri - el, Sanct Ga - bri -
die wal Sanct Ga - bri - el ver - spro - chen.
Sanct Ga - bri - el, Sanct Ga - bri - el ver - spro - chen, Sanct Ga -
fall, dir hat die wal Sanct Ga - bri - el, Sanct

25
- spro - chen, ver - spro - chen. Hilf dass nit
- el ver - spro - - chen. Hilf dass nit werd ge - ro -
Hilf dass nit werd ge -
- bri - el ver - - spro - chen. Hilf dass nit werd, hilf dass nit werd ge -
Ga - bri - el ver - spro - chen. Hilf dass nit werd ge - ro -
30
werd ge - ro chen mein suend und schuld. Er -
- chen mein suend und schuld. Er - wirb mir huld, er - wirb mir huld
- ro - chen mein suend und schuld. Er - wirb mir
- ro - chen mein suend und schuld, mein suend und schuld, Er - wirb mir huld, er - wirb mir huld, er - wirb mir
- chen mein suend und schuld, mein suend und schuld. Er - wirb mir huld, er - wirb mir
35
- wirb mir huld wann kain trost ist wo
wann kain trost ist wo du nit bist, wo
huld wann kain trost ist wo du
huld wann kain trost ist, wann kain trost ist wo du nit bist
huld wann kain trost ist wo du nit

du nit bist barm-her-tzig-kait zu er- wer- ben am lets- ten end ich
du nit bist barm- her-tzig-kait zu er- wer- - ben am
nit bist barm-her- tzig- kait zu er- - wer- ben am
barm- her-tzig-kait zu er- wer- - ben am lets- ten end ich
bist barm- her-tzig-kait zu er- wer- ben am lets- ten end, am
bitt nit wend, ich bitt nit wend von mir in mei-nem ster- ben,
lets- ten end ich bitt nit wend von mir in mei- nem
lets- ten end ich bitt nit wend von
bitt nit wend von mir in mei-
lets- ten end ich bitt nit wend von mir in mei-
von mir in mei-nem ster- - ben, in mei-nem ster- ben.
ster- ben, von mir in mei-nem ster- ben, von mir in mei- nem ster- ben.
mir in mei- nem ster- - ben.
-nem ster- ben, in mei- nem ster- - ben, in mei-nem ster- ben.
- nem ster- ben, in mei- nem ster- ben.

Ardo si

Ar - do si, ma non t'a - mo,
Ar - do si, ar - do si, ar - do si, ma non t'a - mo,
Ar - do si, ar - - do si,
Ar - - do si, ar - do si, ma non t'a - mo, [ma
Ar - do si, ar - do si, ma non t'a - mo,
non t'a - mo, Per - fi - da, per - fi - da, e
ma non t'a - mo, Per - fi - da, e di - spie - ta - ta, e
ma non t'a - mo, Per - fi - da, per - fi - da e
non t'a - mo,] Per - fi - da, per - fi - da, e di - spie - ta - ta,
ma non t'a - mo, Per - fi - da, per - fi - da, e
di - spie - ta - ta, In - de - gna - ment', in - de - gna - ment' a - ma - ta, in -
di - spie - ta - ta, e di - spie - ta - ta, In - de - gna - ment',
di - spie - ta - ta, In - de - gna - men - t'a - ma - ta,
e di - spie - tat' e di - spie - ta - ta, In - de - gna - men - t'a - ma -
di - spie - ta - ta, In - de - gna - men - t'a - ma - ta,

10
- de - gna - men - t'a - ma - ta, a - ma - ta, da si le - al' a - man -
in - de - gna - men - t'a - ma - ta, da
a - ma - ta, da si le - al',
- ta, in - de - gna - men - te a - ma - ta, da si le -
da si le - al' a -
15
- te, da si le - al' a - man -
si le - al', da si le - al' a - man - te, da si le - al' a - man -
da si le - al' a - man - te, da si le - al', da si le - al' a - man -
- al' a - man - te, da si le - al' a - man - te, da si le - al' a - man -
- man - te, da si le - al' a - man - te, da si le - al' a - man -
- te: Ne piu sa - ra, ne piu sa - ra che del mio a -
- te: Ne piu sa - ra, ne piu sa - ra che del mio a -
- te: Ne piu sa - ra, ne piu sa - ra che del mio a -
- te: Ne piu sa - ra, ne piu sa - ra che del mio a - mor ti van - te, che
- te: Ne piu sa - ra, che del mio a - mor ti van - te,

20
-mor ti van- te, Ch'o gia sa- na- to il co- re; E-s'ar-
-mor ti van- te, Ch'o gia sa-na- to il co- re; E-s'ar-
-mor ti van-te, Ch'o gia sa- na- to, ch'o gia sa- na-to il co- re; E-s'ar- do, e-s'ar-
del mio a-mor ti van-te, Ch'o gia sa-na- to il co- re; E-s'ar-do, e-
Ch'o gia sa- na- to il co- re; E-s'ar-do,
25
-do, ar- do di sde- gno, ar- do di sde- gno, e non d'a-
-do, ar-do di sde- - gno, ar- do di sde-gno, ar- do si sde-gno,
-do, ar- do di sde- - gno ar- do di sde- gno, e non d'a-mo-
-s'ar-do, ar-do di sde-gno ar- do di sde- - gno, e non d'a-mo-
ar- do di sde- gno, e non d'a-mo-
30
-mo- re, e non d'a- mo- re, e non d'a-mo- - re.
e non d'a-mo-re, e non d'a-mo-re, e non d'a-mo- - re.
-re, e non d'a- mo- re, e non d'a- mo- re.
-re, e non d'a-mo- - re, e non, e non d'a- mo- re.
-re, e non d'a- mo- - re.